SAMPLER

Sean Ashton grew up in Norfolk, studying sculpture at the Royal College of Art. He now lives in London, teaches on the Fine Art course at Leeds Beckett University, and writes regularly on visual art.

He is the author of the novel *Living in a Land*, a memoir written in sentences constructed in the negative, described by Darian Leader as 'the funniest, most enjoyable thing I've read in years'. His poems and short stories have appeared in *Poetry London*, *Magma*, *Poetry Salzburg Review*, *Artenol*, *Oxford Poetry* and the philosophy journal *Collapse*.

Sampler

SEAN ASHTON

Valley Press

First published in 2020 by Valley Press
Woodend, The Crescent, Scarborough, YO11 2PW
www.valleypressuk.com

ISBN 978-1-912436-39-2
Cat. no. VP0159

Copyright © Sean Ashton 2020

The right of Sean Ashton to be identified as the
author of this work has been asserted in accordance with
the Copyright, Designs and Patents Act 1988.

Cover and text design by Jamie McGarry.
Additional editing by Jo Haywood.

Printed and bound in Great Britain by
Imprint Digital, Upton Pyne, Exeter.

Contents

for Violet and Leo

Preface

IN THE MID-1990s I was part of an editorial team tasked with producing an encyclopaedia written entirely by poets. When the project was first discussed, in the spring of '97, we were convinced that an itemised treatment of the planet that went beyond the usual remit – average rainfall in Paraguay, rice farming in Laos, the evolution of mammals during the late Carboniferous period – would make salutary reading, 'haunting the spaces between the entries already found in the *Britannica*', as I recorded in my role as secretary at that first meeting. The quixotic premise of the venture was compounded by the decision to shelve the projected volume not, as might be expected, under poetry, or even literature, but in the reference section, where, God willing, in addition to supplementing the works of Roget and Collins, it would rub shoulders with the *Britannica* itself.

There were only ten of us, but we were young, impetuous and prolific, alloying our separate minds to a common purpose, generating over 4,000 entries in just six months. Sadly, there were no takers. We considered self-publishing, but by the time the older members of our team were solvent enough to consider pooling their resources, the others had moved on and the material was left to moulder in my study: twenty box files of typed and handwritten oddments. There they remained for two decades till I took a second look last August, curious whether their contents might yet be of interest to the world.

Readers will decide for themselves whether that is the case. I have called this modest selection a *Sampler*. The present classifications are my own. We had not advanced to the taxonomic stage at the time of the project's abandonment, but it seems to me that each entry is at home in its particular slot. Where necessary, I've updated entries to make them less anachronistic, reshaping them to the current zeitgeist. My only other intervention was to replace the personal pronoun 'I' with 'we'. This is consistent with our initial aim. For it was understood that while each entry was written by a single author, the individual lyric voice was subordinate to a collegiate voice, one we all chose to adopt as a basic precept of our endeavour. In light of this, the reader might ask what right my own personal appellation has to be emblazoned across the front of the present book. It's a question I have asked myself, but now that my collaborators have gone on to bigger and better things, I confess to feeling some measure of entitlement to the work as its sometime chief editor. Besides, anyone who has ever published anything knows that in putting their name on the cover they are not so much claiming credit as taking the blame.

Acknowledgement must be made here to the following authors for their donation of sources: Mr Thomas Stearns Eliot for his contribution to the entry on Peaches; Ms Poly Styrene for supplying the last few words of our entry on Polystrene; Professor Peter Osborne for the quotation in the entry on 'Groysing'; and Mssrs Samuel Johnson and Thomas De Quincey for their work on Tangerines. Thanks are also due to the posthumous spectre of Mr Ogden Nash for presiding over Apricots, and to the all-too-humous influence of Mr Donald Rumsfeld in pinning down the essence of the Vibraslap; while Mr Dan Graham's *Time Delay Room* led to the conclusions arrived at on the subject of Installation Art. As to those responsible for the gathering and processing of data in those last days of the 20th century, when everything seemed possible but sadly nothing was, they know who they are and I shall preserve their anonymity.

S.A.

Tresco, June 3, 2019

Fruit & Veg

Peaches

An apple or pear can be consumed while doing something else but a peach requires your full attention. The best way is to take off your shirt, stand over the sink and have at it like the primate you are. To say that it should be ripe is obvious. To say that its flesh should yield readily to the tooth, its fluff brushing your chin as you bring your lower mandible into play, is a point hardly worth labouring. To say that there should be jazz-funk on the radio, kids playing outside, an ambulance passing by at that precise moment, frankly insults your intelligence. Perhaps somewhere else someone is being knocked from their bicycle or fired from their job. Perhaps, as you bite into it, some terrible disaster is afoot, a cataclysm that will later confer on your actions a retrospective insouciance. Do you dare to eat a peach? By all means go ahead. But know, as the juice runs down your forearm onto your tennis shorts, that we shall not come running, we shall not come running with a dishcloth.

Broccoli

As He busied Himself with the finer details of His creation, the Lord our God in all His omniscience can't have foreseen that a stalk of broccoli would so resemble an oak tree to an Englishman named John Constable that he preferred to lay out an entire yield before his easel than have recourse to the preliminary sketches he had made that morning *en plein air*; and as for the claim that Constable might have discovered Fauvism a century before Matisse, had he used the purple flowering variety, we may speculate that Jehovah's concerns were more natural than cultural at this time, that many epochs had still to pass ere He turned His attention to such matters.

Grapes

Much has changed since Rome burned, this bacchanalian symbol long since demoted to a hospital fruit, brought to your bed in a brown paper bag or a carton covered with netting that puts you in mind of a funeral veil, as you lie dripped up and jaundiced, awaiting diagnosis. A decade later, someone arranges a picnic for the birthday you thought you'd never see. 'Here,' says a friend, 'we brought you these.' And it's like you're back there on the ward, praying for the all-clear.

Tangerines

There are some things one can take or leave. Commentators are moving towards the consensus that the tangerine is just such a thing. In its defence, the peel is easily removed, the thumb burrowing underneath like a shrew sniffing out prey, and the segments separate nicely, with a rubbery sound that is just short of sexual. But critics bemoan its low acidity. Johnson describes it as 'an apprentice orange that dare not speak its mind', while De Quincey laments 'the tendency of its flesh to conceal pips, an encumbrance one had every right to suppose would not be there'. Many point to a citrus group already brimming with options (clementine, mandarin, satsuma), though it's true that if a military general is in want of something to demonstrate the position of his regiment in a long-winded after-dinner account of how he suppressed the natives in Abyssinia, a tangerine will do nicely if nothing else is to hand.

Apricots

We have nothing to say about apricots. We have nothing to say about apricots and neither does Ogden Nash, but of the many poems Nash might've penned on the subject, this is surely his finest:

'The question is moot:/Why take the trouble/to go out and buy/this low percentage fruit/when most if not all/the apricots I try//underwhelm the tongue?/Why did Nature create/this compromise/between peach and plum,/this despairing date/ that made glad eyes//at a mango and got hurt?/Who has them on a hot day,/or makes that special trip/to get them for dessert?/Commentators say/they've now become hip//in some neighbourhoods,/exhorting me to choose/this bland victual/as a workout for the taste buds/I ought to use/to keep digestion ritual,//but the best thing, I find,/is to hide them in a stew/or watch them wither on the side/as the week unwinds,/till there's nothing else to chew/but whatever's left untried,//and even then they linger/on the windowsill/or get used as a nose/in a face of root ginger/and dried dill,/a paltry echo//of the corner shop:/stray Arcimboldo/on my worktop.'

Various Polymers & Plastics

Cellophane

Now that you've unwrapped the teabags and stowed the box on the shelf, let it have its moment in the sun, a cuboid phantom set down on the table, discernible as matter only by dint of its magnanimous sheen, little more than light reflected back. But back from what? Admit it: your admiration for this substance has grown over the years, and now that it reaches fever pitch we must add the word *envy* too, for what you wouldn't give to emulate its character, learn something of its ways, shape yourself selflessly to so many things, only to detach with greater finesse by virtue of a discreet gold band, betrothed and beholden to whoever cuts you asunder. Please let's do this again sometime soon with a carton of duty-free cigarettes, some Paris Hilton perfume or maybe a shrink-wrapped record, a 12" US-import of bespoke stereophonic vinyl.

Clingfilm

At the risk of stating the obvious, clingfilm is cellophane that has gone too far. Clingfilm is to cellophane as crystal meth is to speed, cellophane with ambition, cellophane with a business plan, clutching at the rim of your Tupperware with a zeal that borders on manic, an awareness we must call Cartesian or risk understating the matter. Not only is clingfilm self-aware, it knows it is being watched. If this were not the case, if it could not sense you monitoring its performance, it wouldn't try so hard. So really the problem is you. If you could only take yourself out of the equation it wouldn't be so effective, too damn effective for its own damn good and the good of all damnkind.

Polythene

The gardener pings into focus as he emerges from the polytunnel, overalls tied at the waist like a centaur made of two different men, plants left alone now, pressing at the walls, children trapped under the ice, dew already forming on the grass outside where polythene has no dominion, the lawn at liberty to show itself to the squint of a half-cut moon.

Vinyl

The lead-in grooves appear to give the stylus the option of backing out now, while it still can, widely spaced as they are on the record's outer rim. Or do they remind us of those first steps a long jumper takes, at walking pace, before sprinting towards the board? But let us follow it into darker territory, that sonic alleyway created by its mythical predecessor, the pressing plant's propagating lathe, whose needle mined out the spiral seam currently patrolled by its acolyte. Our stylus would do well to light a candle to its ancestor, who even as it harrowed out Captain Beefheart knew it wouldn't hear him again. Look: the captive diamond is reeled in by the maze, throwing out music almost by accident, a by-product of its groping. Odd how it progresses yet goes nowhere, a motionless minotaur in a moving labyrinth, bumping into the label at the record's end, lifted off by human hand, set down gently in its cradle.

Bakelite

Turn over any item and you will find the following warning: BEWARE OF INSTANT NOSTALGIA. A century has passed since its advent, the brown brethren of plastic's genesis consigned to a ghetto of shoehorns, ear trumpets, deco curiosities, a private plethora of artefacts guarded by a mother made of pearl. We'd miss it had we known it in its prime, but miss instead the world we might've known had we cashed in our ghost earlier, ridden the riding boards of Chryslers, fired a Tommy Gun into barbershops, brilliantined our hair till the slick of it was wicked, burned down a warehouse for insurance purposes, shared a scotch with the corrupt chief of police, before going to Confession in the morning and getting it all out of our system.

Polystyrene

It lies there discarded under the tree till our kids tire of their presents, an iceberg capable of being all things. Shine a torch from the right direction and make all the right noises, and it resembles the battle cruiser in *The Empire Strikes Back*, a Boxing Day come-down for the offsprung. One day we shall escape this bondage. Up yours.

Nylon

'This 12lb 6oz specimen was taken from an undisclosed stillwater in Suffolk. It was caught just after 5am with a cocktail of sweetcorn and bloodworm on a size 10 hook, using a paternoster float rig fished over a bed of casters. Four other tench were taken in the same session. This, the pick of the bag, is the biggest of the season so far, but still some way short of Darren Ward's 15lb 3oz British record. The fish was taken on a 6lb mainline with a 2lb hook-length.'

Selected Occupations

Hairdressers

We've sat in that chair maybe one hundred times facing our paltry reflection, magazine in hand, complimentary beverage, head served up on a plastic poncho, but the more we praise their effortless endeavours the more bashful they become, their peace of mind too brittle, their modesty too set, already sizing up the next client as we skip out into the street, their steadfast refusal to see themselves as artists matched only by our willingness to claim authorship of their work, the vastness of their humility completely eclipsing the day-to-day scale of their achievement.

Librarians

Rarely do they stand when you approach the desk. Rarely do they rise and lead you to where the book is located, content merely to smile and point, directing you this way or that. The Dewey Decimal Classification system was devised purely to support their sedentary preference, their lower halves constantly hidden, secreted under the counter. They are public figures of a sort, but only from the waist up, no more seen out and about than the puppet of a popular children's TV show is seen leaving work or standing in line at the coffee place. But this is just a piece of misdirection, for the truth is that most librarians can fly, and their reluctance to do so, their stubborn restraint, is by far their most beguiling characteristic. What else is there to say? They are punctual, efficient, have good personal hygiene, work well on their own and as part of a team, and their beauty conforms to the national average. So let us close the dossier, put it to one side, and never more speak of them.

Jugglers

We've always wanted to say '...and now for the jugglers'. We've always wanted to say, at the end of a speech or poetry recital, '...and now for the jugglers'. Or maybe we'd be in the lecture theatre, and instead of questions there'd be jugglers, and if anyone came up afterwards and said 'I very much enjoyed your lecture' but failed to see the point of the jugglers, we'd make it clear that *we* were the support act, our contribution merely a pretext for something more entertaining. But we don't want to get into a debate on 'high' and 'low' culture. Not at the current time. We've said all we have to say. And now – now for the jugglers.

Waiters

A certain sulphurous charm pervades these basement premises, the burgundy perfectly uterine, the brûlée ensconced in its ramekin, a toilet that will only flush if handled just so, a Polaroid of Le Pen flapping in the window, arm draped over the smiling *patronne*, whose teenage son was destined to wait on our table, stationed in the alcove there like Kafka's lugubrious gatekeeper. Already thinking of the tip – whether the dotted line can take the strain of our inner gratuity, our secret urge to send him off on some Moroccan vacation – we seem to forget that we too begin from a losing position, barely able to pay our share, still less finance Tangier; and after coffee, when we are through and the alpha male calls for the check, we kill our conversation as he brings the chip-and-pin, respecting his transactional rites, fumbling euros into the salver, wondering who came up short.

Snooker Referees

They loiter at the edge of the lamplight, like something out of Edward Hopper, overseeing the laws of a late-night geometry perfected by a handful of men, their occupation even rarer than that of those in their charge. They are fewer in number than astronauts and no less inscrutable than anyone at NASA, one part maître d', one part head butler, with also something of the undertaker about them, especially when the table is cleared and the frame finally won, the black ball potted, the white rolling on like a boy left playing when his friends go in for dinner, Ronnie O'Sullivan turning away for the mid-session interval. We are not ashamed to say we can give you their names from memory: John Street, Jan Verhaas, Michaela Tabb, Len Ganley...

Four Musical Instruments

The Harpsichord

There is really very little that can't be improved by the simple addition of a harpsichord: rugby, snooker, heavyweight boxing, archery, skateboarding, golf. Harpsichordists are natural outsiders and therefore fit in everywhere. It makes no difference what they play or how, the effect is always the same, a jingle-jangle shortcut directly to the id, reaping the latent madness in anything they accompany: the shot put, the triple jump, the pole-vault, the hammer, a glass of water slowly evaporating on a table made of pine. The harpsichord is intense. The harpsichord is bipolar. The harpsichord is a piano without a superego. Harpsichordists have no comfort zone and rightly kick sand in the faces of pianists. Pianists are to harpsichordists as pilots are to astronauts: folk who fail to achieve orbit. Never mind that harpsichordists can't get down again. Never mind that they can't achieve re-entry. As long as they keep playing they'll be fine. And there is no reason why they should want to come down, is there, no good reason at all.

The Accordion

Where the harpsichord is an all-purpose instrument, accordions must be used sparingly. They are ubiquitous in Balkan regions, but the Balkans know what they are doing. Croatians are particularly adept, Kosovans also. Serbs are not that fussed any more, they seem to regard it as a peasant affectation, counter to their embracement of modernity. But let us imagine we are in England, if that is not too much to ask. Here, the accordionist must be sensible: it is no use his prancing off after hen parties as they parade through the precinct in their silks and fine arrays. It is no use his prancing anywhere, his act is too melancholic. He should sidle instead. He should sidle up later, when drink has been taken, and his cap shall fair brim with pence. But even then he must time his misery to the second, retreating into the shadows at the first suggestion of tears. Not all accordionists are swarthy and not all accordionists are male, but a female accordionist is rare. A female accordionist is rarer than a female drummer. If you find one, you must do all you can to keep her, for she is jauntier than her bearded counterpart. We are lucky enough to have our own. She follows us everywhere, moving her bellows in sly syncopation to our mood.

The Double Bass

An ogre would put it to his chin, but a man must angle it over his shoulder like a cat cleaning its hind leg. And that is not the least of his worries. For he must also offer up a solo, his bandmates trailing gently off till he is the only one left playing. They seem to come from elsewhere, those adenoidal notes, foregrounding background mood, like a man's voice heard at night from another room, your father's low monologue as he finally says his piece, your mother all talked out on the pillow. Look how hard he has to work just to make himself heard, yet somehow he survives the spotlight, saxophonist leading the applause as the drummer comes back in. His force is weaker than gravity, but remove him from the quartet and the others drift off, into the jazz nebula, noodling away in five-four.

The Vibraslap

It used to signal a plot twist, the butler not guilty after all, the broad in the liquor store smarter than she looks, the policeman clearly an impostor, and even today, when Tarantino can't foreshadow a shitstorm, the vibraslap guy still gets the call, chartered directly onto set, but for the most part his CV makes uncomfortable reading and he must eke out a living on nature programmes, where his contribution is largely ironic. And it *is* just the one guy, like Ken Morse and his rostrum, career peaking in 1980 with TV's *Worzel Gummidge*, the show about the scarecrow with several different heads, the vibraslap here coming into its own as the definitive sound of intrigue, the sound of known unknowns on the point of becoming known.

Birdsong

The Lapwing

That certain contemporary pop singers like Miley Cyrus and Britney Spears use Auto-Tune to modulate their voices is a poorly-kept industry secret. What is often overlooked in these discussions is that the lapwing has a similar device, albeit one bestowed by nature. The bird's crest, sometimes mistaken for an ornamental accessory, is actually a pitch-bender, without which it would be hard-pressed to produce those plaintive wails of electrified distress so characteristic of the British countryside. This, briefly, is how it works: when the bird flies into the wind, the crest is blown back and the voice rises, and when it turns away from the wind, the crest is blown forward and the voice gets lower. Mid-ranges are achieved by angling the head side-on to the prevailing breeze. The science behind it is fascinating: a complex system of transistors and valves housed in the bird's breast converts the turbulence into analogue signals which are then transmitted to the beak. The results, however, couldn't be further from the work of Spears and Cyrus, bearing closer resemblance to the tonal signature of the 1970s synthesiser, as heard on 'Xanadu' by Rush or Kraftwerk's 'Neon Lights'.

The Goldfinch

If you take a trawler across the North Sea to procure a handful of diamonds from an accredited merchant in Amsterdam, remove them from the velvet sack and drop them down the plug hole in your hotel bathroom from a height of five feet, taking care to empty the entire contents in one go, you will find the sound they make as they tumble out of posterity's reach not unlike a goldfinch's spangled song, the sound of something small and valuable decadently squandered, a bewitchment of riches flushed into oblivion. And did we mention that the diamonds should be cut? Did we say that each one should be faceted, just so? That the sink should be of granite, the fixtures and fittings gleaming, the penthouse floor of finest marble?

The Nightjar

Such is its recent surge in popularity, we now operate as the nightjar's UK agent, shepherding folk to the heath at dusk to see this summer visitor. Some have compared its call to a moped, a distant churr mistaken as reptile or dismissed as the carry-on of insects. But listen closely and the ear is tricked into more outlandish comparisons: a Geiger counter in Chernobyl, the refrigeration unit on a Scania, Lee Scratch Perry twiddling knobs, a looped sample from Stereolab – every analogy falling short, for it resembles nothing but itself. The sound increases with the blackness, and we have to tell our protegés that *that's it*, what they are already hearing is what they have come to hear. When the bird finally shows itself it is almost too much: off they caper, waving the white hankie someone has told them to bring. As we grope our way back to the path, we explain that the birds are on loan from Sinai, that the Bedouins look after their foreign rights but we represent their interests here, we are their man in England.

The Starling

A part-time poet has this to say about the starling's contribution:

> Cruise ship crooner in avian form,
> you offer up the latest hits,
> finches, warblers, thrushes and tits
> all dipped in the oil of your song.

We get it: the starling is prone to imitate other birds. What the poet does not tell us is that his lyric was penned in a state of belated remorse, thirty years after having shot one with an air rifle as a boy in 1983. It is this that his quatrain seeks to conceal though he will doubtless try to tell you otherwise. But we like what he says about oil. For the bird sounds much as it looks: glossy and iridescent, a black brush loaded with many colours.

The Magpie

A certain brand of toy machine gun lives on in the magpie's chatter, a brown plastic model manufactured by Hasbro, if memory serves. It may seem that we have this arse-about-face in putting a manmade artefact before Nature's own, but the magpie concurs, the magpie approves, increasingly urban as it is. Indeed, the magpie conspires freely with gentrification, often the first on the scene in a hitherto neglected area. Sometimes artists move in, only to find magpies have already set up shop. Unlike magpies, artists have no song, and no call either, shaping their mouths around something that may or may not be a cry for help.

The Built Environment

Houses

One of the many benefits of civilisation is the division of land into plots, the building of houses thereon, the subdivision of houses into things called rooms, the confining of certain activities to these various sealed-off chambers, and though we have tried cooking in the lavatory, butchering meat in the lounge, there is seemingly no way of returning space to its basic volumetric state, no way of reclaiming the versatility that preceded its subdivision into things called rooms, which, as we have learned, is a consequence of building houses and dividing land into plots, one of the many benefits of civilisation.

Roads

A road is all gutter if you take into account the camber, puddles stretching from centre to kerb in the event of flash-flooding. Rain is a road's fiercest critic, revealing imperfections, inconsistencies, shoddy workmanship, though it does so through constructive dialogue, like a therapist or someone leading a workshop. But we have doubtless picked a bad example, the tarmac laid down in haste by a short-handed crew working to a deadline. So let us turn our attention to the motorway, which allows us to travel at such speeds our tyres convert its texture into braille, transmitting via the steering wheel what we should think and feel. A smooth road may lend efficiency to some thoughts and oversimplify others, while a rough road can sharpen our focus, a rough road can keep us honest, so that on reaching our destination we know exactly what to say, though it must be added that a man arriving at your barbecue may have nothing more to tell you than the story of how he got there, which exit he took, which junction he came off at, and how he'll get home again once you've persuaded him to leave.

Streets

For her school project, our daughter was asked to pick an aspect of the city and describe it in 100 words, and this is what she came up with:

> For my project, I am writing about streets. A street occurs when one building flags down another building and bids it rest awhile before continuing on its way. The resting building is so smitten by the other building it decides to stay put, two buildings now standing where one resided and before you know it a whole row has ~~sprang~~ sprung up. But sometimes it happens that the second building isn't persuaded by the first, sometimes it's the other way round, sometimes the first building goes off with the second building, disappearing over the ridge, and then there is no street at all, just a massive hole in the ground.

We don't know if it's strictly ethical to appropriate our daughter's work in this way, but we like her use of the word 'resided' rather than 'lived', we think it shows promise, we think she may be something of a writer.

Cobwebs

Every spider's a bull's eye from which a dartboard flows, the results conforming, by and large, to a single silken blueprint, Ruskin's hope that we should build forever here enshrined in an evanescent craft. We commend the arachnid's integrity, its workmanlike manner, the shared ownership of the means of production, above all, the truth to materials. It's an International Style and no mistake, but remember, it's machines for death we're talking about here, not machines for living. The results may look elegant but less is not more, mess is law.

Stations

We repeat the same journey every day, but still it seems we never arrive, the 8:08, the 7:35, it makes no ounce of difference. At day's end, the Fat Controller picks up the concourse and shakes it like an Etch-a-Sketch, well understanding that to find ourselves back where we were, nothing lost or gained, is the best we can hope for, a magnificent achievement, really, the most cherished of all things. And this chap here, coming towards us now with a machete, he understands it too.

Cladding

Sometimes it happens that a man without a jacket is given one to wear by the casino. Tower blocks are also clad in standard-issue garb and they too must wear it whether they like it or not. The difference being that one gets to decide whether to play roulette while the other does not know it is already playing.

Furniture

Stools

A chair will bend over backwards for you but a stool is really not fussed, aspiring as it does to a non-sedentary role: reaching a book on the top shelf, propping open a door, fending off intruders to the family home. Stools are not passive. They want to be involved. Show them your backside and they regard it as a threat, they think they are being punished. A stool can go six years or more without being sat on and still hold out for the lion-tamer. Obviously, all stools long to hook up with the lion-tamer, but few achieve this objective. A stool might conceivably end up in a museum, as an example of itself, and there are worse fates, but expect it to exude considerable chagrin as it sits there, in a glass case, alongside its counterparts, however the curators dress it up: *Stools Thru the Ages*, *From the Milking Stool to the Piano Stool*, or whatever. Check out the barstool. Seriously, check out the barstool. The barstool has it about right: screwed into place, going nowhere, realistic about its chances, nothing if not philosophical about its scope for future progression.

Beds

A hundred reckless sleepers were asked to express a preference and all came down firmly on one side or the other. None chose the middle and none claimed to alternate, and even if they had, we wouldn't have believed them, for the bed is like a city with two football teams, Manchester, Glasgow, Rome, Madrid, no one able to quite remember when their loyalties shifted and they came down decisively on left or right. Some folk guard their side jealously, and should a couple conspire to produce an infant child, this can be placed between them as a bulwark. Another metaphor has it that the bed is *The Raft of the Medusa*, your partner a peasant posing for Géricault, getting into so many positions over the course of a single night as to resemble every shipwrecked soul on that accursèd vessel. We don't like either metaphor. The first is too sporty, the second too bohemian.

The Sofa

Time was, one could not speak of the sofa without speaking of the television, but the television is no longer an item of furniture, the veneered lantern of bygone times demoted to a flatscreen travesty, or else entirely absent, usurped by tablet and laptop. Historically the television has exerted authority over the sofa, dictating where it goes, which direction it should face, and even when it should be occupied. This tradition is now coming to a close, and we'd like to sign off with a cosmic analogy to mark the pathos of its passing. At some point in the future, the Sun will leave Jupiter to run the solar system on its own, and so it is here in the living room, where the sofa must take charge, learn to adapt, or go the same way as the commode, footstool and ashtray.

Transportation

Tricycles

Even now that canals are cleaner and villages have no dumps and there's no longer any chance of seeing one dashed against a wall by boys with nothing better to do, lobbed over the fence of the electricity substation by the backwards kid egged on by the others, tricycles remain the most tragic and forlorn member of the velocipede family and perhaps transportation in general, tragic both in motion and at rest, brand new or second-hand, stolen or lost, operative or faulty, souped-up or standard, children's or adults, though an adult's tricycle is a far worse crime, a tricycle aimed at adults is a grotesque abomination, and we invite all those who feel otherwise to form a convoy and beat a three-wheeled path to our door.

Trains

The boy in the wheelchair likes to watch trains. Here he is now on the platform, clapping and laughing, ecstatic, his chaperone standing nearby. He is brought here most evenings, thrusting his body up out of his chair, addressing the carriages personally with shrieks and hoots and a braying sound that comes instead of words. It is tempting to believe that if he could talk he would tell us what makes trains tick, but for all we know this repertoire is sufficient to answer his needs, an eloquent response to the thrum of the engine, the slamming of doors, the stationmaster's whistle, for all we know it's his muteness that allows him to commune with the rolling stock. We would add further that it's only this boy who makes us aware that there *is* a train, such is the monotony of our routine, that he does us the service of showing us our lives. But we don't really know what that means. And why say it, why say it if we can never make him see it?

Teleport

Before joining the Away Team and beaming down to the surface with our phasers set to stun, one of the questions one might ask, one of the issues one might raise concerns the impact of teleport, the long-term effect of the body's dismantling and instant reconstruction on one's personal wellbeing; and while we're on the subject, while we have your ear, another quibble one might have, another note of caution one might sound vis-à-vis the Away Team expedition, is whether the colour of our sweater, different to that of the captain, whether the colour of our sweater, different to Spock's and McCoy's, whether the colour of our sweater, different to Sulu's and Uhura's, is an instance, an example, a case in point of what is called 'narrative foreshadowing', the planet being hostile, after all, its natives quick to anger, and the man in the red sweater seldom returning, seldom coming back to the *Enterprise* alive; but such questions are rarely asked, such matters rarely broached by ordinary Starfleet officers, such opinions seldom ventured by those who have chosen, those who have decided, those who have gone so far as to go boldly into the unknown.

A Few Liquids

Blood

Delays are occuring at Junction 7 of the Common Carotid, corpuscles backing up as far as the Left Subclavian. An accident out on the Right Radial has resulted in slow-moving traffic around the Palmar Arch. The Renal Arteries are also struggling to cope with the drive-time surge, heavier than usual due to unspecified problems in the Extra-epidermal Area. More on this when we have it.

Iron

On planets where iron is found only in liquid form and in great surface abundance, rivers and lakes running deep and wide with the stuff, and on which there are no towns and cities, no streets, no buildings and consequently nothing we could call a 'room', one would be hard-pressed to argue that iron is a solid at room temperature, the elemental basis of industrial civilisation, your alien host laughing as you explain that where you come from a whole age is named in iron's honour, that from its atomic structure have sprung cars, girders and anvils, that from its constitution have been wrought railways, locomotives, ocean liners, though the vessel in which you've paid your visit, the odd contraption from which you have just tumbled forth, is built mainly from titanium, vanadium and other non-ferrous metals, your own planet having left this era behind some time ago and entered its terminal phase, the phase in which its residents have no choice, no choice but to strike out in search of new worlds.

Stains

RE: stain on kitchen work surface, May 14th, 2017. After much consideration, we have decided to make this stain permanent. In order to demonstrate how clean the rest of the kitchen is, we have decided to leave it in place and work round it. We want folk to look at it and reflect that the world is never more charming, never more delightful, than in the moment before it becomes changed, never more charming and delightful than when a part of it is wiped clean, never more charming and delightful than when someone gives the order and the bulldozers move in. The stain itself is not all that: a chance spillage that happened to dry in the shape of Madagascar. We don't even know what it is. Coffee? Tea? Oxtail soup? Anyway, if we could work round it, if we could all pull together on this, that would be great.

Mercury

A spillage of mercury is somehow obscene. Mercury has no more business leaving its confines than Howard Hughes does his hotel suite, going out into the sun and waving his hands in the air. It rightly abases itself at the feet of Celsius and bristles at the mention of Kelvin, who had no use for quicksilver, even as a way of describing the footwork of promising young footballers. Without the thermometer it is nothing, nothing but a metaphor waiting to happen. The thermometer is equally beholden to mercury's liquid allure, no more capable of supporting itself than form can survive without content, no more equipped for the solitary life than a writer can thrive without horseplay, without a little flight of fancy from time to time, of which we have now had enough, quite enough for one morning thank you.

Clothing

Hats

Let us pass over their practical use and assay their other applications, for we have all thrown it into the ring, have we not, we have all offered to eat it, have we not, and what we wouldn't do for you at the drop of one isn't worth writing down. We have already spoken of doffing our hat to certain deserving individuals, and shall very soon have to speak of clamping it *back* on our head in the event of meeting someone who *doesn't* command our admiration. We noticed that the England captain failed to remove his helmet on scoring a fifty against South Africa in the recent test match at Trent Bridge. This is disappointing. As captain, he should be setting an example. Or perhaps he had his reasons, perhaps he was hiding something?

Shoes

Our shoes never quite go with the occasion, and on those occasions when they do go, they go rather too well and the occasion has no choice but to disown us, eyes travelling from collar to belt, from there to the hems of our trousers, frowning where man meets earth: spats, loafers, sandals, brogues – it matters not what comes between the planet and ourselves, the thinnest of membranes preventing the defilement of the former by the latter, or the latter by the former, as the case may be.

Summer Dresses

Women sometimes have cause to regret putting on something lighter, something they hardly feel on the skin as they go about their business, but whether they get it right or wrong, wrong or right, right or wrong, there's a feeling it has to stay on, is there not, there's a feeling they must go through with it, and should the day turn and their legs run cold and their clavicles start to chatter, they would no more have that day again in a different suit of clothes than a mayfly would return to its larval stage, trussed and overcoated in the maggotry of winter, looking up at the pond's surface, shaking its claw at a half-timbered sky not quite ready to receive it.

Blouses

Remember blouses? Those flammable things that girls used to wear when it wasn't OK to go out in whatever: polyester breastplates with padded buttons securing ample fronts, sleeves that billowed like Fletcher Christian's, a whole furlong of piping, superfluous slits, false pockets, a delta of misdirection, and always something borrowed on the lapel, dragonfly or artichoke of tarnished metal, cheap brooch filched from a stepmum's sternum, something to lose on the parquet floor when she led you into the mossy alcove several Malibus hence.

Some Poets

Minor

Not to be confused with the marginal poet, the minor poet is usually remembered for a single great poem, a flagship sonnet that had to be written and chose a certain author. It can seem, in such cases, that the minor poet was visited by the Muse only once, when the Muse was short-staffed and needed someone to take dictation. It's pointless asking the minor poet to repeat their act, for even if they knew how, they would not do it for you again. But you are right to ask about 'their other stuff', as you call it, you are right to ask why they still bother after the Muse has clearly left the building, for the truth is that minor poets *choose* not to write great poems. And the poems they write in the Muse's absence are not, in fact, minor poems, just poems in a minor key, though now we come to think on it, it's all minor, is it not, or would be without the pizzazz, the various set themes, those many fluttering particulars that somehow anchor the general, the rose and the nightingale, crow, lark and linnet.

Major

Major poets are mocked by minor poets in the same way supporters of football teams funded by oligarchs are mocked by supporters of football teams not funded by oligarchs, which is to say, disingenuously, for they well know there is nothing to stop someone putting the Orient back into Leyton, or the Argyle back into Plymouth. Why, you yourself, the proud disseminator of a mere handful of stanzas, could end up Collected and Complete, on a stage at Hay-on-Wye, folk piling into your tent ('Come on, let's go and peer at the brute...'), while Norman Lamont reads Kipling next door and Houellebecq sighs at his interviewer for the twenty-sixth time, the best writers of his generation destroyed by boredom and bottled water, on overcast midsummer days just such as this.

Marginal

The marginal poet is talented enough but rough around the edges, and always – to use a sporting term – 'unproven at this level'. One throws him in at one's own risk. The elevation of a marginal poet to a major verse anthology is not unlike the selection of a volatile county cricketer for a forthcoming test match, one in which Donne and Shakespeare will again open the batting, with Larkin coming in at No. 3 when the ball has lost its shine, Gerard Manley Hopkins to follow, Plath at 5 and Dickinson at 6, while Beckett keeps wicket as usual, coming in at 7 when the game is won or the situation quite hopeless – or 8, depending on whether we go with Stevie Smith as a second all-rounder or Linton Kwesi Johnson as a fifth bowler, capable as he is of moving it around when there is sufficient cloud cover. Fanthorpe is picked for her off spin – we don't know if it's going to turn yet but she can hold up an end and is useful with the bat. Mick Imlah impressed on debut and opens the bowling with Bukowski, assuming Bukowski is fit. Is Bukowski fit? Call him. Call Bukowski. Ask him if he is fit.

Occasional

The occasional poet is not always a bad poet, even when reacquainted with their pen after an interval of 30 years, in response to the death of a loved one, say, or that of an English princess, though the outcome is always at the mercy of the occasion, reluctant as they are to stray beyond its purview, deaf to anything non-diegetic, blind to intertextuality. And now please leave us alone, if you would, to make sense of what we have written, for we are far from experts ourselves, wont to dress the plainest of brides in ostrich feathers and motley.

Experimental

We can only tell you what we have seen with our own eyes: one chap offering a blank manuscript, only to be accused of verbosity by another presenting the ashes of a manuscript, accused in his turn of being bourgeois for placing them in a receptacle when he should have scattered them on the wind – this from a man who had eaten his own words and not even documented the act, simply allowing it to circulate through rumour and post-medium intrigue, all three playing a key role in *Helping the Avant-garde Become a Truly Historical Phenomenon*, forthcoming on Peyote Press, POD edition.

Performance

The festival crowd don't really do poetry but seem to enjoy hers, the way she owns the stage like a West Coast rapper, surfing the Severn bore of public sentiment right back to its source, especially the girl in the bikini top and denim cut-off shorts, perched on someone's shoulders there, there in the sun-soaked mosh pit, who approved of the last band and now approves of this, approves of everything all day long, arms ending in Satan fingers, anode and cathode of a demagogic charge. We lied: there *is* no girl in a bikini top who approves of everything all day long, she exists only on the promotional poster, but there is a performance poet, there is a performance poet, and she's killing it, killing it right now here at Platitude.

All Sports

All Sports

All sports are equally futile so let us pick one and have done with. We spin the bottle and it points at rugby. What has rugby to say for itself?

> The egg-shaped ball is deliberate, not simply the nearest thing we could find to a sphere, a collective handicap all must embrace or seek alternative recreation, the unpredictable bounce a necessary chance element, the spark of chaos that ignites any given game. Whatever, it works for us. Then there is the scrum. Let us say immediately that even we don't understand it. You may've noticed that the referee talks to the players constantly during the game, especially during the 'breakdown' (as it is called), telling them what they can and can't do in the ruck and the maul (as they are termed) even as they are doing it. This is because no one is quite certain what is going on in rugby at any moment. But the referee is trained to be slightly more certain, or slightly less uncertain, than the players, explaining it to them as they go through the phases (as we call them). Rugby is a sport in search of rules, an activity in search of limits, as controvertible as life itself in its sundry manifestations. But its main appeal is that teams progress forward by passing the ball backwards. If the shape of the ball is the work of pranksters, this is the intervention of a poet.

The bottle landed kindly. Rugby has spoken well. Rugby has spoken so well, we needn't seek the testimony of any other sports.

All Rock Bands

All Rock Bands

All rock bands need a name. Everything needs a name, but rock bands need one more than most. In short, rock bands are not most things and must convey this in their name. In the 1960s a collective noun was usually preceded by the definite article – The Beatles, The Kinks, The Hollies – but it has since become acceptable to use a single noun or adjective – Crass, Rancid, Discharge – or a memorable phrase to signal something stranger, something altogether more compelling. High court judges must be careful here. To render Suicidal Tendencies as *The* Suicidal Tendencies is to lead members of the jury to believe the tendencies have been ratified as suicidal by a special committee of Suicidal Tendency Ratification, when no such committee was ever convened. As for the *in*definite article, this is comparatively rare, but highly evocative when used discerningly. One thinks of A Flock of Seagulls as an obvious yet delightful image, and one thinks of A Certain Ratio as the first words of a sentence rather than the name of a band, as in: 'A certain ratio of one part cement to one part sand and three parts gravel is required when mixing concrete, but we failed to follow this rule and have since had to relay our drive.'

Three Black Holes

Cygnus x-1

●

Messier 104

●

MACHO-99-BLG-22

●

One Noble Gas

Neon

Neon is shy by nature, withdrawn and unresponsive, but unlike krypton and argon has learned to overcome its condition, all but promoting itself to the rank of a solid to secure its place in society. Its collaboration with glass is quite remarkable, hailed by chemists and physicists alike as one of the great double acts of our time, its luminescence signalling all manner of commerce, its pulchritude matched only by its turpitude in leading men astray, arrowing into dive bars, pointing into casinos, embroidering brothel windows even as it dignifies the edifices of ecclesiastical bookshops. As to its place in history, that is no less certain, secured by artists who choose to work in what we might call the modern style. Many candidates spring to mind here, but we must single out Mr Bruce Nauman, specifically the 1972 work *Run From Fear, Fun From Rear*, which renders in this noblest of gases a glowing vindication of sodomy.

Medical Science

Neurology

He won't leave till he gets some answers, and there is already a trace of truth issuing from his right hand, raised level with his left for comparison: a distinct tremor that may or may not be you-know-what. The neurologist hands him a doodah and asks him to draw a whatchamacallit, having first demonstrated with his own doodah how the whatchamacallit should be drawn. The neurologist's whatchamacallit is perfect but the patient's is inept, as might be expected from one who has not drawn a whatchamacallit in years, or indeed handled a doodah, and who may or may not have you-know-what.

Physiotherapy

Turns out the pain is all his fault: he's misused his body,
must learn again how to stand and sit, be taught to exist
differently or compound the error. It's a novelty at first,
not being him: habits corrected, posture realigned, he goes
through the motions gladly, submitting to the new regime
like a promising dressage horse. Quite when the rider is
thrown is difficult to say. But one morning he is whole
again, an organism destined to fail, a centaur in spirit, a
man with a tale to tell of how nature had its way with him
– not once, but twice.

Pathology

He wrote it down on his own corpse during the lecture on Kristeva, large capitals inked into the hand for want of a piece of paper: *AN EXILE WHO ASKS 'WHERE?'* Hours later it's still there, long after he's shaved and showered, put on a clean shirt and died under a bus. In the next lecture, Roland Barthes tell us that language can't always be taken as read. The words are gone from his hand now, which is how he knows he's dead, how he knows his time is spent, how he knows what Kristeva meant.

Art & Language

Painting

The collection is on permanent display, each painting in its own bespoke frame, like folk in their favourite chairs in a home for the care of the elderly, but no hope of death, only decay and a steady trailing off of interest, reignited by daytime visits from unfamiliar relations, people who want to relocate them, move them to another room, claiming they'll be happier there or at least that the change will do them good. They meet our gaze gamely enough, no more dodging interpretation than patients can duck diagnosis, but there is something sad in the contrast between the mercuriality of their process and their final fixed form: their inability to evolve still further, beyond their author's intent. They begin as ideas, paintings, growing slowly into artworks, only to turn into artefacts, and when they appear at auction it is as though one's own grandfather has been dragged from the cemetery to attend one final orgy.

Sculpture

When trying to corroborate the story of the Cleaner Who Accidentally Threw Away the Item of Modern Art, we regret to say that the cleaner in question was unavailable for comment, while the critic's claim that the item never belonged there in the first place but was likely put there by someone who, quote, wanted to test the boundary between art and everyday life, unquote, is really not the kind of thing that appeals to our readers.

Installation Art

The installation does not try to be beautiful. The installation does not try to be beautiful and neither does our description of the installation. It is claimed the installation is political. It has been put to us that the installation is political. But go ahead, see for yourself: enter the installation. What do you find at the centre, what do you see but a video of yourself entering the installation, what is served up but an image of you, just now appearing onscreen, what is being produced here but the transformation of yourself, a unique person, into Someone Just Entering an Installation? It doesn't matter that it's you on the screen – anyone will do, anyone will do to complete the installation. Look at you: you went in as yourself, and now you're just anyone, nothing more than a person entering an installation. But we did warn you, we did say that the installation was political. As we pointed out at the start, the installation does not try to be beautiful, and neither does our description of the installation.

Philology

Perhaps only a philologist, a travelling philologist moving from one place to another, moving regularly from one place to another in a modern European democracy, eating in chain restaurants and staying in budget hotels, watching TV and hearing folk having sex through the walls, perhaps only such a person, only such a person as this, would reach for their pen one evening and write the following poem:

> The Greeks have a noun, *hapax legomenon*,
> Meaning 'a term used only once',
> To name, as it were, a unique phenomenon,
> Bypassing all those savage grunts
> That do for more ubiquitous stuff.
> But every phenomenon is surely unique:
> Words reshuffled only repeat,
> And no speaker ever has enough
> To reconstruct what they think they saw
> And resurrect their phantasm.
> Take this hotel, the room next door,
> These two humans close to orgasm,
> An upshot that will always sound
> Like it's happening for the first time,
> Even when its grist is ground
> On matrimonial grind.

Or perhaps there is no travelling philologist, no budget hotel, no humans close to orgasm. Perhaps no such poem shall ever be written, still less circulated in a modern European democracy.

'Groysing'

The cat likes to rub its cheek on the corner of the book while we're reading in bed. Cats will use any protrusion but ours prefers books. Difficult theory is his thing. Like us he has got used to it over time, acquiring a taste for Chantal Mouffe and poststructuralist philosophy. He is hot on Brian Massumi and other elucidators of Gilles Deleuze, but craziest of all for Boris Groys, 'the master of Slavic nihilism'. It may be something in the binding or the paper stock favoured by Groys's publisher, may even have to do with Groys himself, laudable as his work is. But in many ways that is by the by. For there being no word in the English language to designate this feline habit, Groys shall lend his name to it, and we shall henceforth call it 'groysing', and should we run into Groys we shall explain what we have done, and more than likely part as friends rather than enemies, returning to our respective lives with a sense of mutual enrichment, at worst mutual indifference, never to see each other ever again this side of Purgatory.

THE MEADOWS

Published in 2021 by Golden Hare Ltd.
68 St Stephen Street, Edinburgh EH3 5AQ.
mail@goldenharebooks.com

ISBN 978-1-8384065-1-6

THE MEADOWS

i

Mist – and it shows; between St. Catherine's Hill
and other figures in the landscape. There
they wait, cathedral, school; but from St Cross,
out past a world's-most-scenic cricket square

the Meadows do not show. Nothing stands still.
The cottage-trees Keats saw here with their moss
and windfalls vanish. There are streams, a path.
And though I'm in my room, I dream I'm here…

I dream my fathers – figures round my hearth –
will catch a scent of home from their prodigal son
and greet me from far off as they return
back through the mist…
                        Yes, dream it; bring them near –
have father glad to breathe his son's dream breath –
and, Pirie, talk to me – about your death –

ii

Others knew first. Not my turn to be told,
round Pirie's circle went the shock. It spread
more than the news – it seemed to squeeze the news
each time friends passed it on, more hard, more cold –
that loving cup, that sip. The unspeakable, said.

The Meadows where we'd strolled just lately, whose
gin-clear chalk streams looked their April best
just would be where he'd seemed – not that depressed;
litter there made him talk about despair –

but grief and guilt I feel indoors, alone,
insist – it's me – I should have known it first,
guessed before others ...and forestalled the worst...

but there's an order grief can't change; queue where
I've got to wait, to hear the news by phone.

iii

The phone rang upstairs. *Robert! Good to… I'd
not been expecting…!* Unawares then, kind
questions of mine about him ran out. Blind,
I took the force of Pirie's suicide.
I backed off, not to face it – squirmed, which came
to heighten his grief, someone you could trust;
I dithered; asked if he'd got the right name,
said someone else's could have been mixed up;
he said he'd check. At which, in me, it must
have started working, then, if not at first.
I put down the receiver like a cup.

And looking back, it's still there, like a thirst.
He was my friend – and father, I suppose;
he couldn't die. That spring we were so close.

iv

Time flew there by the phone. Our time, a life
shared, vanished; shared since that night when I'd read
Waller's 'Go Lovely Rose!' in the old School.
Then it was just a poem dear to me,
we'd stood in public – not like man and wife
(the school mag pussy-footed 'round a bed
where Waller's muse pets mine, the flirting cool').
But someone heard me speak the poetry.
A small man with thick glasses, dressed in black.
It's hard to look the audience in the eye,
your pathway dark, breathing the poem's breath,
like Orpheus you must trust and not look back.
It's hard to live and look at those who die.
You act, they watch: the old play – Love meets Death.

V

Now death is in the poem. Life's curse of
unfinished business, as the therapists say.
It's on my scent – I want to get away –
I've got a son myself, who needs my love –

he's one year old, just walking, Tommo or
Tomito – laughing, weeping little elf
who loves me; one day must he blame me for
this hide-and-seek – this peek-a-boo we play – ?
Now that he's here I've got to find myself.

Such recognition comes, they say, in stories.
Our old selves dream, yet they're the ones that tell
the tales that will not die: lives blocked… the way
it hurts to wait forever… bankrupts…worries…
All move on when a story tells them.
                                   Well…

vi

after the reading, for the first-year boys,
Pirie came up to me; told me he liked
the piece the way I'd read it. And his voice
moved me – his firmness ushering what he thought
through random check-point stutters – my heart ached
as his head tossed, impaired delivery brought
wisdom out shaken in a little rage,
but instantly I liked him; liked the wise
definite words escaping from their cage.
He liked my reading (liking, twisted, ties),
what's more, he asked, did I *l-like* the stage?
W-would I act in his play? I couldn't wait –
(though I'd not heard of Ibsen, and was fat)
for Betty Bernick, plump, rouged, in a plait –

Months passed… we passed, twice, smiled, I tipped my hat,
he taught the top sets English (I had learnt)
so it felt like an honour, earned or not,
one spring day in my pigeon-hole, his note
fixing audition times…*and if they weren't*
free, he'd be pleased to see me at his home.
Home! I felt human in that school, and wrote,
but met him in a hall grown brown with grime,
its motto tarnished (Manners Makyth… gloom).
There I read him 'If you have tears, prepare
to shed them now…', my best piece at the time.
I think of him; and silence shows me how
far grief has come, from schoolboy days of flair
for grief, to tears men shed with no words now.

viii

There were two other candidates (he thought
he could discount them and gave me the part).
Day after day scenes came right: time, that worm
cut daily, thrived: Day One not only brought
our first rehearsal, but another start
wonderful for a town boy to confirm
there in the chalk-stream, just below the bridge
fixed like a jewel – a trout. It wouldn't budge.
Each day I found it there – till, close to tears
thankful, incredulous, I called it a sign –
a live brooch pinning Pirie's life to mine.
That spot that fish loved. Weeds there now rehearse
a scene for me… That pulse of cool thrilled space,
they let their hair down – feel it – still in place.

ix

A brief life-story Pirie can't hear now.
But something we both recognised would grow
made this our play. He said I seemed to know
the way he thought rehearsals ought to go
was never late, was natural on stage
had confidence to put my heart to work
at woman's sorrow, loyalty – and rage;
yet there was one notch more we'd never mark,
truer to life. What Pirie faced was real,
his wife, friends said, miscarrying their first child
that same week. Could our play have helped him feel
equal to bear this? Could I act her grief?
Could two real things meet, somehow reconciled,
if loss on stage caught life the actual thief?

X

I had reviews. My father quipped, "Not bad".
I wrote back, in block capitals – I HAD
TO BE AN ARTIST. He had not replied,
what could he say? He feared the pull of school?
I feared he thought I'd joined *the other side*,
'wise cash, wise comfort' was his family rule
so he said nothing, left art in the air,
and chose the wisdom of a self-made man.
Self-made! Then who made me? I read Flaubert
where pure art outdoes dad's dynastic plan:
I felt misgivings about how he'd sit
and plan life by my bedside, how he'd say:
"Darling, look out for boys with any wit,
make them your friends. You'll give them jobs one day."

xi

At first I'd loved the closeness, found it right,
thought nothing better could be done on earth
than help make him, my father, more secure;
after scant school he'd taught himself, at night,
– from Russia, but a British Jew by birth –
copperplate writing, geography, literature,
while working day times to pay boarding fees
for siblings – played the father to his dad!
My mother loved the gift she said he had
for brotherhood, and care. I knew all this.
But in my world all friends were refugees,
with Pirie came that voice all exiles miss...
my lips stayed sealed: two home-truths in one heart,
I had no words for that, till out came ART.

He never took my classes – it seemed meant,
our year was not the academic year,
nothing was done that wasn't our free choice;
I liked his kind rich mind, he liked my voice,
I'd take big summer parts, a king…a seer…
Shakespeare, Keats, Ibsen, back our drama went…
That Pirie introduced me to John Keats
whose verse I'd never read, showed me the way
the best things linked – Keats's life, set as a play –
first the boy frowns, then thanks to Pirie, meets
a great imagination he would love.
I'm stalled now. Search life's old map from above –
something to salvage – make do now the street's
been bombed, with wreckage, verse, some still-hot stove.

xiii

The day *Keats* opens, my First Night, our French
teacher falls ill. The class cheers. Pirie stands
in for him. While we wait, I doze…Wide lawn,
a window…calm grass… mower… then – a wrench
back to see Priday – rearing with both hands –
a redhead – wild – twice Pirie's size, all brawn –
shunt several desks to block the classroom door.
Pirie's shrill sing-song, *he'd a c-class to teach!*
but while he called, the class had work to do
in sham French, mocking stutters, high-pitched speech –
Zen, l-let him een! He came in. I abhorred
how that class stood. Mock form. All stood up for
my friend. I'd just stood by, while Priday roared.
Well now it's out; it took two to taboo.

Our three *Keats* evenings ended. But I'd known,
I'd found my poet. His *"My creed is love*
and you are its only tenet" his *"The Truth*
is what Imagination on its own
figures as Beauty" – shone in lights, above
father and plush green wing-chairs of my youth
where he sat sagely planning out my life.
"Give up French, when you leave", (French was *'a whim'*)
"Choose Economics". *Money helps and heals.*
Then smile. Joke. School French spreads well 'like a knife
through butter, earns no bread'. Yet crossing him
I knew crossed Keats too. *Ideas unlock deals,*
use your Imagination. Stymied, he
found ways. Imagination was his key.

And if Keats' gorgeousness made dad look mean
what ached was not a simple rift between
father and art, this child of seventeen
saw something complex: "My life, in the grips
of dad's imagination, is his Beauty…'
I felt I understood – not greed, not duty,
dad was a poet to his finger-tips
but shaped me for a world that wasn't verse
or true at all…in honest ways…to mine.
If I could split, things I loved could combine,
stars could sleep soundly in dad's universe
on meadows sweet with bees and warbler-song;
but if I scorned him, I'd be lost, and wrong.
Imagination was our family curse.

xvi

I stopped my night walks in the Meadows. Then
Pirie put on *King John*, with me as King.
I was due to leave the coming spring
and if I'd never act for him again
I knew we must stay friends. In time I'd learn
to drive, and dad, who planned the best for me
would help me 'mix with nice types' with a car;
and in that Vauxhall Super I'd return
from Oxford wits to mugs of lime-flower tea
and other gifts our future held in store.

Rehearsals brought one final closeness…I'd
failed him at last, got tonsillitis, and
Pirie says *"Get well! Or I'll have to s-stand
in for you!"* When I think that you'd have tried –

xvii

I think straight of your father, close with grief,
telling me of you knocking at your aunt's
front door: you'd finally run away from school,
sorry, lucid…trembling from relief…
"I don't like Monsieur x, the one from France, he
shouts at me and pulls my ears; it's cruel after I've
said I'd try to do my best!"
That ogre, from your childhood, was it him
your life his play - your part a little test,
him, marking *wrong* your wish to pass it well – ?
That angler-fish where love can't see or swim,
able to make life seem no good to you
Perfectionist! Did he send you to hell?
The school you finished with, was cruel, it's true.

xviii

And there was more to tell you – of King John.
I feared the Last Night Party for the cast.
My dad's not like you – now you'll meet – at last
after the final curtain – up he'll swan
*I'll be exhausted, greasy…*How I feared
you and my pa would just not hit it off;
he loved to hold forth, wise-crack, play the toff,
I knew you'd not respond. But he appeared.
You stood there, with him, on cue, nose to nose.
I saw dad speak – then stamp his foot, hard, on
the stage – saw you stare at him, rapt, the way
you'd looked years back, with my 'Go, Lovely Rose!'.
I came up, heard him speaking from the play!
Dad knew, by heart, a whole scene from King John!

xix

And in me as he spoke, two private dreams
broke surface, sure as Shakespeare's words: twin streams
plunged abreast there – the whole of me was real –
those things I thought kept you and dad apart,
something of you ran, from my father's heart
to meet me, see you, watch his face, and feel –
"Of all things this is not 'a self-made man'!
I marvel at your father…if you can
then he and I will heal the split in you
as fathers should. As fathers we bequeath
our blessing, friendship…" It told me, I knew,
that now my dad need not be opposite –
this meeting here, twelve years before his death,
would last – the Last Night Party settled it…

the night when Shakespeare, you, and father spoke.
After he's stopped reciting, you had asked
how he had come to learn *The Mercy Scene*
all through, word perfect; he then cracked a joke
which you had laughed at but had soon unmasked.
His mum, who died young (how long lost he'd been!)
had loved these lines – at night he'd lie in bed
hearing her read them, always in his head;
he'd liked the way stern Hubert, charged to sear
the tongue-tied prince's eyes, had found the heart
to spare the child and stand up to the King –
though he had thought the scene was from King Lear!
We laughed at this – and mirth gave each a part,
Hubert, the prince, and John – we made a ring –

where now I saw my role was real: King John,
wanting the good child in me blind, thought art
could split me off from father. Hubert's part
I'd meant for you, but when the scene went on,
the Prince in dad had wept and won your heart,
this spared the vision of the child in me.
By kindness Bad King John had been set free.
It was a Mercy Scene. Your lack of side
had done it all. "How strange life now must seem,"
you wrote to me after my father died,
"…to lose so rich a personality,
someone whose son it must be hard to be,
I shall remember him for a long time."
For both of you a child has cried and cried.

xxii

I in the end played Hubert too. Tough-guy
served a king's grief. With Pirie dead, I flew
into my room, and got the irons hot.
What mercy saves a child's eyes? I forgot,
I sat forgetting; grief would blind; grief grew.
Dawn came; eyes closed, I'd no more tears to cry.
A glow, like touch, spoke, softly, 'It is I'.
A happening touched upon me.

                            Who finds who
when dawn comes? I don't know; verse I remember,
a light, a lake… Not dad, not Pirie, but
the water-meadows – mapped on my distress –
whose story must be kept to that September
and not lumped-in with theirs in case their glut
of life should muddle this life-changing *Yes*.

xxiii

Come to the water-meadows; where chalk-stream
trout hide in summer's glare – where some boys watched
through polaroid glass, or hooked them in mid-dream.
Fix polaroid eyes, like me, on the stream of your heart.
See loves, all we love, die. Death's outrage. Scream
at death, its crime – sky high.
                                    Love. Death. I botched
my As, not fit to analyse great art.
Next term I took up running, death-on-my-back,
ran with a rage which roared with summer gone –
the truth was on the Meadows' cycle-track
and round St. Catherine's Hill – I'd grit my teeth
for love to stave off death, but felt each crack
go through my plimsolls smashing apples on
the path as if my heart was underneath.

It sometimes breaks through, the simple message…

A young man running, each day, not knowing why, but searching nature like a parent's face as he runs; seeing each plant, each tree, looking back like an old-fashioned German doctor. The downcast eyes, the head shaking, a little motion, left and right, the diagnosis of its own death. The young man, driven by love, asks his heart which of the two is stronger, love or death, day after day; interrogates nature over the water-meadows, up Double Hedges, crosses the by-pass, can't go on but goes on, his feet again on tar up Morstead Hill, his legs pink, almost running on the spot, yet getting to the turn where it's all downhill, a grass valley called Plague Pits, some loose-strife, colts-foot, but as he looks, every plant looks back with its death held up like a traitor's head, but still singing, always singing they are loyal to life, they still love being here…! Back down Double Hedges then over the river past the bird sanctuary, Falloden, and through the water-meadows…so much evidence of nature alive, he could not doubt the courage with which love goes to its death, acknowledging everything, its luck to exist, its flourish, its miracles of made…

xxiv

That boy could have been me. Each day I ran.
Each day I saw a bleak ravine, gold trees,
up Morstead Road, downhill home past the San
(a smell of bile to greet me always there),
scholars in black gowns, red blood on my knees;
and in each plant and tree seen alongside
death broke through love, death broke through greenery –
I stared like cameras-full of film, my stare
came back blank – all the green that happened died –
each blade of grass. I saw the film in me
damned like a doctor shaking a heavy head.
No way could love save truly mortal things;
I touched a whorl on my thumb, skin truly dead,
I couldn't get the doctor out of my head.

XXV

Doctor was priest. Death's slow sure pride of place
was morning prayers. Each day the calm massed school
would kneel before him. As I watched the boys
it was death's head I saw in every face.
I filmed the sight, death happening on a spool,
the peace of prayers, like soft earth dug by noise
before then after, brought then hid again
lives full of love, dug out, with the death exposed.
I knew I would die soon. Kept my eyes closed.
Till my last day. My last thought came. A pane
of glass seen caught through final sun on choir.
Stained crystal-cast light. Strange antique blue fire
very fast at first, which poured down cliffs of glass
the way sea-waves replenish, did not pass,

xxvi

it held. I stood there filled with this fast light.
The speed grew till the things I fastened on
slowed down, spread out: the rhythms, the wave bands
of sun, some deep slow ray this sun must throw
now let me cross a line, from day-lit sight,
eyes like a camera taken in quiet hands,
to light come from the heart, moved slowly, shone
from love to things in stillness, to and fro.
The whole world here, no need now to explore,
sight falling calm, heart having time to feel,
my eyes took me towards it but not scared
not needing priest or doctor anymore,
heard the school chaplain tell the school to kneel
and couldn't move, and stood unseen, and stared.

xxvii

I walked west outside Chapel and turned south
down Seventh Chamber Passage, and then out
past the paved School, across the Meads, to where
the water-meadows in September sun
stretched out. I had to be there, had begun,
faced like a hatched fly into September air
Keats' ode – To Autumn. My tongue moved about
Season of mists with my heart in my mouth
the poem like a path Keats beat for me
alive, pure voice, and there frail as a fly
my love of those lines known by heart that day
seemed to belong to each reed, swan and tree.
A vision in which I must live or die
possessed me. I said yes. And had no say.

xxviii

It happened many years ago; and art
and life have never shown the trust in me
that they did then when all of nature knew
I was in love. The water-meadows shone
but not in the light of the sun. The reeds, trees, swan
in Dian sky stood primed since first dawn through
with light, a lake of light – swan, reed and tree
all, like a father, like a lake, but heart
too vast for me: the strength in Keats's lines
came to my aid like oars my heart could feel
there in my hands, frail on that lake and yet
I balanced in that poem's disciplines
and, like a scull, the verse skimmed this too-real-
to-bear-deep-light. Under radiant sky, I set

xxix

out, buoyed, weighed to the gunnels, couldn't capsize;
Sky sang like my mother's joy: to come on board,
a glance would add it, one little glimpse of this sky –
I give this up-glance: everything floods to my eyes –
takes everything with a *whumph*. I sink. And I
step out of time. A vacuum burst, each word
underwater in light, there, reeds – trees – I – before
called something, had no name. Light was our state
like stars, and all so simple with the mind
equal in words to nothing. Verse whose time
held strong, where I could breathe, moved rhyme to rhyme
Meadows to human peace of the starlight kind.
I spoke and saw reeds trees swan – verse…create
love's two concentric spheres. There at the core

xxx

I looked out on the Meadows – stretched an arm.
It shone past difference – outlines knew they burned
away from within, that rules by which things live,
where bark, skin, leaf, divides, break like a charm
before this real light there in things – returned
when I step back – my ground all I can give,
the void but safe – my ears deaf, my mouth dumb
with love remembering its original verse,
there, lasting, gone, the way stars know the night –
that reeds trees swan include me in the light
while the song lasts; flesh verse and Meadows come
outdoors in joy; whatever universe,
it knew the same song light was channelled by,
this Meadows light, the poem of the eye

xxxi

at peace with every step to the poem's end.
So close to them, my heart no longer runs
to try to grasp the feel of trees, reeds, swans
lit like the stars; nor doubts when words descend
the stair of Keats's ode their verses climbed
back to the earth, that these words also know
they served that stillness, joy – joy's being so;
nor how peace breaks in Keats's last line, timed
to say goodbye, to verse, to ecstasy
but with that heartbreak self came back to me
the feeling I was giving up the ghost
the hand that felt was slipping from the glove
that kept it safe. But verse... which touches most...
through which I felt light twice – both heavens, of love

xxxii

and suffering – was twinned too. A two-way stream,
love's double helix, or like Jacob's dream
going in opposite ways, some up, some down –
all through its life, verse knew what dying was.
It sang the supreme praise of joy because
the vision knew the flesh would be outdone
that was that deal love struck. My arm-pits throbbed
my breathing burned me, heart could not keep up –
with life – or not! – what if my body failed!
I loved this world where eyes were flesh and sobbed,
where verse whets thirsts that throw away the cup.
I would pay down this loss beyond repair
with all my heart, joy's dues would be fulfilled,
brought back, almost to earth, the threshold stair,

xxxiii

where heart comes back to sunlight. Threshold light
which shows in things that love their lives. A coot
plucks up its courage, rushes up a stream
throwing wide sky-piped ripples out of sight;
a trout that kennels in a willow-root
stares through the eye-wash of a perfect dream.
Love has not ever harmed these living things,
the redbreast sows more Meadow as it sings
and just enough young swans to make a quorum
vote to rebuild their ruined year-old forum,
where made for change, the mind in every reed
agrees that points of green grow back from chalk.
There will be songs next spring. For now we need
to bear the sense ants in their granaries talk,

xxxiv

and gathering swallows twitter in the skies.
And there the poem ended.
                            In dismay
I saw, walking a dog, coming my way,
a don – economist, with my father's eyes.
We passed, he looked away, not to approve
the vulnerable gaze I meant as love.
Talk was taboo. But still, I thanked him, whom
I knew, who knew that I was out-of-bounds,
who hadn't asked what I was doing there.
I did not know that answer anymore.
I knew my life had changed, the dark before
the whole show shone – love's outcomes – everywhere;
one leaf could kill me with its light. Keats' sounds
had kept me safe. But was now in my room.

PART TWO

XXXV

Not looking back. Till years on, Robert phoned.
Room where I lived to hear how Pirie died,
under a train in London; tell my wife;
a room of sins which can't go un-atoned.
I stood there like a bottle broached and cried
as though I had it in me, Pirie's life,
and he had mine in him – self split apart.
It seemed the same for her, a room like guilt,
or time turned bad by our dear era's death.
Life left the room; my cabin-fevered heart
cooped-up with memory, grieved. The good time built
begun in Meadows with my autumn breath
shared by those living swallows; now, this spring,
the bad, the call, phone primed, about to ring.

xxxvi

I wanted to wear black when Pirie died.
My spirits fell and spread dark wings to match
the sunlight's sponge, the air light never lit;
my own black sun soaked up the light outside
to grieve in what the real sun couldn't catch
till loss was space, and looking into it
a dove of hope which couldn't return home
went searching, like a dream, in deepening piety
like nightfall on a wartime aerodrome
where grief sends upward an exploring ray.
This lazar cruised me, calling, night and day
but found no rest, for loss was vast as space.
Day's many mealtimes passed, past gloom, past gaiety,
my food was memory now and grief saying grace.

xxxvii

Now I look back, with my son one year old,
on father-figures, on the Meadows, yes,
but still trapped in this room. I cast Yeats' cold
eye from the window: there, in the square below,
Shakespeare, Keats, Pirie, father; nonetheless
I must try writing something to provide
answers – or trust – or hope that buds. The show.
I think this story's for my little son
and speaks of joy in him, and art beside…
Pirie, let's be professional! Read your part,
I'll do mine, not the best we've ever done
but the most feigning. I still feel your life
bringing the whole dark house down of my heart
whose mortar death has scoured out with a knife.

xxxviii

Read this. An Oxford evening. My last year;
with father figuring large; less time to share
with you. Since April dad had moved away
to live in Gib, and I would week-end there.
I'd felt fraught all day, came home lost, unclear
found the door open, heard a record play:
and sound like angels danced on that needle's pin.
Like watching vaults build upwards from above
word order, wit, and weight bearing – Shakespeare in love –
sonnets… first showing me where buds begin,
a voice to follow like Eurydice –
then, rooms of air, where Shakespeare paced, railed, breathed,
writing his Will – within which, wealth for me –
a way to see my life. A path, bequeathed.

xxxix

Its ink still wet, the voice said, now, don't start
your father's work; don't make a fortune, found
a school where children can learn Keats by heart,
now what I couldn't do was what I learned.
I lost dad's wish for power, for planning life,
left my gold pen, his gift, I took a knife,
trimmed a soft pencil and then tried to write
a sonnet, not to Shakespeare but to dad.
Not great, but that was fine, on my *doodle pad;*
then did two better ones, in bed, that night,
to Pirie, honest like our heart-to-hearts.
A sonnet, it said, *gives my body strength –*
a time-worn pattern shapes my chaos… art's
eight lines, then six, ten syllables in length –

xl

To Pirie (i)

Dad's love's my jail. There's only you to tell
Pirie, how, though I now need to rebel,
tonight! from love I've fostered since a lad
I look (at last) like him…we both look sad.
No poets can live close – that's him and me,
if closeness thwarts a brain-child of their own;
dad dreams up business schemes – his poetry –
for me it's now a task for words alone.
His has to do with his rough-diamond roots,
but I am like him in opposing him,
he found his own dad's ideas quaint and dour,
my grand-dad was a *cohen*, bought new boots
rather than share dad's taxis, called dad dim
to take mad risks. But their rift hurt for sure.

xli

To Pirie (ii)

Perhaps, as you've said, his great hope for me
that I should carry on the world he's built
brought me too close to know him. Stuck like glue
just now, just as I've got to hurt him. We
love one another – but mine's now part guilt,
the mess love makes of things breaks my heart too.
Life craves for oneness; me, at one with life
that morning in the Meadows made this split.
I feel it, pulling me from dad, from friends...
Do all the hard-won best things end in strife?
You'll understand. Find me the piece to fit
this jig-saw made by love – you're where strife ends.
You moved by this, you writing back to me
will fit my Shakespeare sonnet to a T.

xlii

And Pirie made time for us two to meet.
I'd not flown out to Gib the next weekend;
when we talked in the Meadows, heart-to-heart,
he didn't shatter like some vase of Keats'
he was the endless gift of life, a friend.
I drove home feeling less obsessed with art
and more with living friendship – someone's love
that shares the crisis, true regardless, beats
a friend-to-man that breaks. Life, not an urn.
And yes, it may be wrong to be obsessed.
To be obsessed how one small group, above
no man-sized coffin-rig or winding sheet
would stand and part in love fire could not burn,
friend, in your ashes, in your urn; 'At Rest'.

xliii

But friends spring life on friends. First that next year
I'd shocked him, asking him to referee
for applications sent from Germany
to leading merchant banks. "Not that, Oh dear,
not banking…won't the best goals disappear
if men of sense in nineteen-seventy-four
start working life in capitalism which
seems on its last legs anyway? The rich
can't ride much longer on the grossly poor.
Still I might be quite wrong – we schoolmasters
have strange ideas. In fact I'm thinking of
giving up teaching, going in half-shares
with someone's farm in Wales. From Winchester's
prestige, and strikes, to self-sufficiency. Love."

xliv

We'd both got grounds to give. I asked him, *Why* – ?
The month before he left our school, in his
book-laden don's house, plant-books standing by,
he said his piece on towns: false hierarchies,
something about his mother's wisdom, how
a true life had to be lived close to the land,
was what he'd always felt. The time was now.
But lots of people didn't understand.
The school head – just retired – now boomed: he viewed
Pirie as an eminent son of art
and art required cities. Shakespeare's law.
One Christian blamed him for ingratitude
ditching the school that made him. Have a heart,
both of you, I say, *beasts don't gore and claw.*

xlv

Before his flight from towns, though, I'd explain
my weaker truth: banking was all I'd got
just now, to fill that 'England Expects' slot.
I'd use dad's will to front my own with (pain
hadn't the heft to shield my writing – dad,
as pleased as punch that I'd try banking, had).
When, Pirie, all your life your father's dreams
have hedged you in, like Sleeping Beauty's briars,
the first-come prince lacks what real art requires,
Avenging tearful child! – this reader screams –
best let briars grow and Beauty stay asleep
till you have written something to wake up to.
You know you haven't yet. Hands tied…and cupped – to
shield your dad's dream candle – while you weep…

xlvi

But he did not break his side of our pact.
Asked if he understood, my father smiled
and told me how the well-spring of his life
had been his liberty – *to choose, and act* –
and he'd 'not wish a scrap less' for his child.
He'd made his own choice of his work and wife
and always coped, and done what he enjoyed
so, if I worked a full year at the bank
and wasn't happy, sure, he'd understand;
with my background I'd not be unemployed.
Employed? I gulped. What job? That page was blank.
My job was compromise. What Pa had planned
left no stand-by. 'To flop or to combine!'
A toast in hope and fear, my two-grape wine,

xlvii

which went to my young head. My interview
for International Finance. The man
who, if I got the job, would be my boss
had asked 'Was I ambitious?' It felt true
both to be honest and reply in verse:
Romantic verse, a toast to him who ran
the bank, he'd know what he was taking on.
The lines – which sang but didn't answer straight
(I was ambitious, to make both lives work) –
conclude, the souls who live were those who strove.
This made the German boss smile, mutter 'bon'.
The words were Victor Hugo's, and those great
gusts of French feeling worked for that young Turk.
But the job-offer was not signed with love…

xlviii

My dream then, to be true to self and dad,
was tested; by the year-end it had failed.
It made me, Pirie, think of what you'd said
of capitalism, but what truly ailed –
what seemed now on its real last legs, was us.
For though my zeal, or loyalty as his child,
could get me through the same long hours as
the bankers, this job sorted out the men
from what I was, a child uncharmed by toys.
The whizz-kids round me made their serious noise,
I wrote bond-memos with my dad's gold pen;
but someone my age did them all again.
After six months my boss said he was 'fussed'.
A year on… *My son? And so prodigal!* Bust.

xlix

My mother fought back. '*Of your own accord?*'
and blamed me: I'd been too strict with our pact,
First years are trials, you're young, you can afford
to soldier on. Two years; then think of leaving...
I didn't want to face her with the fact
I'd got the sack; *in sack-cloth, mother; grieving;*
it isn't always real death makes you feel
you've lost a friend, the mourners can come too
when everyone you know is still alive.
The child you thought you had in you seemed real,
yet, like the dead, you know it's gone; dream you
must, somehow, learn to get along without.

That child went down with the dream ship. And I've
no job, and now real life blows me about.

1

I'd lived dad's dream to show him banks could mix
with poems. Mission failed. I blame my dad,
then blame myself – no verse, no failures, nix –
that he'd have wanted, even if I had,
what he wants now, my plans for my career. Dear
life! – He'd hogged the choosing up till then -
careers were his department, his idea –
he'd steered me so I'd grown up, yet not grown
except in guilt; his fault I'd fibbed when asked
how things had gone at work and seen him beam…
Behind my smile a two-faced child was masked –
half glad, half sad (I mined one loyal seam) –
it was his fault my lies worked for his gold.
But when his face fell, when the truth was told,

li

the child who loves his father still feels guilt.
Shrinks, like a washed-up spider. Poetry
ran, Pirie, like a pipe, to drain revenge –
spider... dream... the dynastic myth dad built –
his money stayed. It fed and watered me.
The art world's pay for poems was small change,
that's how he liked it, cash: the cards he dealt.
His face on all my coins, washed underground,
the man in me now felt bought-up by him;
the self-made son lacked spunk below that belt.
And yet, though no financial feet were found,
a little spider must have learned to swim
in your Welsh farm, joys not for trifling with,
and climbed back up the spout of family myth.

lii

Where comedy (dad's word), its love, its guilt,
got me an audience in the week he died.
That family evening video, with him wrecked
by chemotherapy, all Broadway stilt
and slushy songs and white smiles. I'd not cried
for him, felt just too mixed-up, I expect;
the film – Cole Porter favourite – set between
death-bed and heaven, gathered speed to fit
a tragic final song and parting scene…
the last song, 'Do I love you? – Do I!'
                                                    Lit
there on his pillows by the screen, he sang
words often said, but sung now in the gloom
this meant *Goodbye,* this kitsch show-room
swan song. I said I thought the doorbell rang.

liii

And went into the bathroom; locked the door.
Hebrews might say pearl tears shed in a scream
crown pity like a queen to be wept for –
the way I'd blamed him that I'd lived his dream
then blamed him that I'd nothing in its place
the years we'd rowed, three years I'd hurt him with,
worked as a messenger so I could write,
his son! A post-boy! What a slap in the face!
I wept – in terror – *Let him have his myth! –I loved
him, needed him to live that night! –*
and looked then in the mirror. Not at me
ask all the pills for pain massed on the shelf –
I saw the old Greek mask of Tragedy.
There it was, O. And pity; queen; herself.

PART THREE

liv

Pirie, you know, through these three lost years, you'd
become for me a sort of ideal dad;
one I thought I'd have chosen if I could,
in whose life's meaning I could still believe.
It seemed my fate to find my father's bad.
But there were loopholes – gaps through which to grieve –
Pirie could give me hope, but not achieve
that last night of King John, that mercy scene.
He read my 'powerful' verse and wasn't keen;
and I helped him plant hawthorn trees in Wales.
Those Welsh nights! Made for owls, for thrilling through…
my ear hushed, on dad's brow once, heard this sound
through silence, when he read me fairy-tales…
But Pirie needed my affection too.
He got depressions. In the spring, he found.

lv

But I recall the first spring night, when west
weather was flush and drink flowed with no end...
first visit to your farm, a climate's test
in rain of the man-child for the teacher-friend,
I'd phoned from the M4, said I'd be late,
the rain was buoyant, but I heard your voice –
conjured you up – and if you couldn't wait,
Eva would, and the cats. You were awake:
I pushed a light-chinked door, and still rejoice
how you fell on my neck, how you were glad,
"Caro!" arms spread in open give-and-take,
which I returned – stunned that I'd come to hug
the greatest teacher that I ever had.
Then slept, by seed potatoes, in a rug.

lvi

Next day was fine, and in the next ten years
we sampled all the seasons, made hay, cut
the wheat that waved with flax-flowers round its ears,
golden in August, green in April, but
never so lovely as that harvest time
when while we mowed girls sang behind our backs
and in straw-scented downtime we'd relax
settled on stooks, watching the late bees climb
the cornflower blooms like sun behind the hill.
In May the bluebells, and the daffodil,
the nearby droves of wood-anemone,
the flowering of just looking at a flower.
Small-holding you could stroll round in an hour,
each bud you passed, there like eternity.

lvii

I didn't grant spring's life its grievous side.
Of course I feared the work might be too hard
but that you'd get depressed, feel dark, ill-starred,
that wasn't till the year my father died.
Your father told me you had not been well
and not just this year; then, I thought, we'd talk
down in the nursery where we'd always walk
in spring. You'd check each tree. Young leaves in sheafs
now serious, like brows frowned in shock: you tell
how in these valleys farming-folk in spring
suffer depression often, drown their griefs
in drugs. You'd done it too. What did I feel?
I said I thought it might take art to bring
balance back, steadier thoughts. With art, he'd heal.

lviii

So while you checked – not trees, I thought – but books,
returning life the way trees flowered...? I wished
now for your spring cure, time off from the farm,
to read, who knows, to write... We exchange looks,
my compliment for which you hadn't fished,
but when you told me it could do no harm,
you'd take time off and work on Lafontaine,
I told you what had been so hard for me
to comprehend – that friends I so admired
were not all secret poets. Love and brain
were all it took, and there'd be poetry...?
And your attention thrilled us all, inspired
like birds from trees, no lie, like Orpheus' lyre...
You said: I am a humble versifier.

lix

Repeated, in a letter, with your thanks.
I'd helped you with some fables. Humble? Yes
and great, your Lafontaine in English verse –
helping with which I felt rewarded twice,
the master giving power to the boy
like with my one-year-old who crows and swanks
when I let him spoon-feed me baby-rice
as if joy meant dad's power in reverse;
but a more complex and sufficient joy,
each for the other's good; a phrase I found
you liked – but liking (pride hard to disown)
was changed to pride in work which egos cloy
when said by you. Us, making up some ground
dad groomed me for but had to work alone.

lx

Like fields and streams the farm contained your verse...
We drank rosé d'Anjou and looked at notes
up in the orchard with the early bees,
their cleansing-flights like boys off to rehearse,
the freshness of the Welsh air in our throats,
Lord Lambourne apple-blossom on the breeze
and you were better. Verses, if not true,
had given life fresh hope, like what you grew;
farming for you meant being all you were.
I'd long thought of you as a pioneer
for good life – pure soul but advanced somehow:
sustainable life few could sustain now,
but one day many might take your deep breath –
trust towns without them, and not die your death...

lxi

Perhaps with more help you'd have lived and stayed.
What was it, what aloneness, made you leave?
Eva and you, your father, and the kids
who'd baulk at farming in that sun-rise world
where high technologies and scopes unfurled
new service industries in social grids,
nuclear family at whose centre cleave
a married couple, loyal, a bit afraid
getting older, running low on money –
rates, electricity, and water cost
more than comes in from selling eggs and honey…
but most of all, the future on your own?
You must consider carefully when asked
if you'd like your job back, your old black gown.

lxii

Perhaps there was no other way. How, though,
how far the thing would fall from what you guessed:
the Head, who offered you this job, retired
soon, and *who'd come next*? You wouldn't know.
It was too soon, but must be for the best.
Nice you were still remembered and admired.
Far off, the verse I read at your thanksgiving
heard by the new Head. An old colleague. Right.
His Lennon specs, blurred with his tears and breath;
you newly dead – him, me, when you were living
you cast together once before, to cry:
a scene from Long Day's Journey Into Night,
that full moon in the Trades, high dim-starred sky – !
and then – the curtain fell. Now this long death.

lxiii

Last day I saw you, stretched out on spring grass
feeling warm sun in silence through closed eyes,
I'd come out, first just sat then done likewise,
against my lids watched those quick bright flecks pass
like germs of life between two slides of glass
lit for the microscope that magnifies.
And if I magnify what life made dear
the strange quick flecks of memory with me now
I may be wrong, perhaps I stand too near,
when earth is pain – and thinking like a plough,
but let me say this, friend who's left the farm,
I still believe what's sown in good hope grows,
the seeds Jack trusts, thrive, as the Beanstalk shows.
Seeds sown in fear bring harvests that do harm.

lxiv

You left school life in hope; came back from fear.
Friendship could not change fact, but could undo
a blindfold. Lost in Cardiff, one spring day,
we'd gone to the museum, seen the Van Gogh
Late Cornfields in The Rain…the soul as weir…
disturbed, I scribbled lines, you did some too –
and that was your start – like with Keats…the way
chance moves us from one to another love,
your eye could write – it seemed your lines on art
could hold a mirror to a painting's heart
changed by your vision, true to your surprise;
you sprang, like you'd a cat-face – painted on –
your voice became a thing before my eyes,
a creature in you, a chameleon.

lxv

We walked through Cardiff's park and parted there.
Over our heads the cherry blossom burst,
incalculably rich pink – pleat and flair –
I'm smitten by such things. But you spoke first.
How much you didn't like such spring excess.
A thought occurs I'll say now and digress –
how since your death your friends try to explain
what went wrong as some deep need to suppress
the feminine in your heart. Well, maybe, yes.
The blossom was like fear, desire and pain,
your caged intuitive that scorned your brain,
those petals like a ballerina's dress.
Perhaps it's death to go against life's grain
up falls like salmon – love meets death again.

lxvi

And thoughts come back of Hubert and the prince.
Something that Shakespeare meant, not quite worked out
you, clear-eyed, tragic-hearted henchman of
a king, whose crime you've owned, and died for since
because you lost the heart, or nursed the doubt,
and self-hate took revenge on your self-love...
I call the prince the spirit's feminine
because she weeps, has his fierce joy in life,
and does she love you, Pirie, do you know it,
does she? Yes, like your children, me, your wife.
But from the dark you were not happy in
I see a fearful ruling masculine
suppress the light-in-darkness – prince or poet –
henchman and child both killed with that royal knife.

lxvii

I still think of the life you did dare own,
filed near me, your twelve works on works of art;
poems on Poussins, Bruegels, Le Lorrain,
in verse now it was you, not Lafontaine,
in verse a sinner may throw the first stone:
a masterpiece you liked you'd take apart
and move about as if it weren't complete,
only to come full circle on your tracks
your path brought home, amused and moved and wry.
Like Bruegel's Adoration of the Kings
as *Hay-Stack Joseph* and *Frog-Face Sergeant* meet
behind *Gauche Child* and *Podgy Virgin's* backs:
Care, child, you say, get up and go. But why…?
That spy, that tip-off, and those halberd things…

lxviii

but at your death, there, with that painter's dozen,
a new poem left art dreaming, miles away,
set on the farm. It touched the life you'd lost,
strong, strict and quirky ('graze on' rhymed with 'blazon')
based on an autumn vision: leaves being shed...
but rapt, that morning when you broached the hay,
stood watching eight cows munch in the year's first frost.
Hearing, then seeing, ash-leaves fall... not dead,
thrilled in one joint cascade, yet separate too,
how small ones rolled down slopes in the air like kids,
over and over, cheering in twists of wit –
I'm seeing something deeply seen by you.
It might be your eyes under my closed lids.
The farmer's shoes, the cap death doesn't fit.

PART FOUR

lxix

Pirie and I have come full circle now.
I told the shrink I saw after his death,
the Meadows vision met the writer's art,
both dealt with love and death, in both, somehow,
a death lets out a light that's underneath –
walking with memory, making a new start
into a world frames can't, but must, contain,
art wasn't neat, a boundary in the brain,
but in league somehow with the Meadows light.
Some sense. Somehow. Pirie would want to know
precisely what I mean by what I write.
You stand for meaning, Pirie…but you don't,
your story lets its light out from below.
Life was the frame and made an end. This won't.

lxx

Talk – letters – verse – and dinners. The next brief
months – lead to London, and into gallery art,
nice pretexts: "Poussin's spring times you can't see
in Hampshire". Odd short trips, a night away.
We'd part at Paddington, but spend a day
united in the National Gallery
where time flew, with a painting, heart to heart.
With him I learned how Poussin made from grief
his *Dance to the Music of Time*, then one thing more.
Our last scene. I'd come back to my empty car
still warm with one I loved and drove it for,
felt it grow cold, then shrink – as loss met pain
like some Dutch winter street scene where the rain
blows in the snow, the door of a home ajar

lxxi

with sadness. Not great Poussin, Claude Lorrain…
but true, and mine; the quick goodbye of friends
beside a train, the hug one free hand flings,
cheers for our friendship, plans to meet again,
the parting happy each sad heart pretends
as life goes on – brave Dowland song it sings –
yes, 'grief was there made fair, and passion wise'.
Yet wrenched, when both are wrenched, loss unifies.
I'd felt a sudden breakthrough. Time that splits
fell away from my heart as we embraced.
Then came the one, most-true, kiss of my life.
Through gaps in a hedge of clothing Pirie fits
his lips upon my neck, so surely placed,
it brought the dance to my then world and wife.

lxxii

The smallness of the space inside the car
put framework round that joy; it tipped the scales,
reckoned the loss, as, oddly, looking far
into a landscape as we'd done in Wales
can make you feel you need the photograph
to close what's just an uncontainable void.

Today we'd looked at Poussin's 'Golden Calf'
there too, the truth of human scale destroyed
by people who thought nature worked for gold.

I couldn't drive, bad luck and somehow old –
I'd walked beside his train – it went too fast.
I'd let it go. The image racked me…till
it came back, when my dying dad was ill,
how cancer, like this, picked up speed at last.

lxxiii

I sat and wrote. He sat and went southwest.
Verse coaxed shapes from the life, breath into scale,
the nail fate's hammer hit was not a nail,
but joy, come to a head: the fun, the best
at last – he'd left his wash things at Moss Bros
which made us late, we'd tripped, I'd ripped my jeans
running to fetch them – shamed at Charing Cross – !
but stood soon with those earthly-perfect scenes
of Poussin. And he'd asked if Poussin's map
of ideal time made sense of life's real road.
I joked, no, life makes no sense without Claude.
He died next month. Embankment tube. At five.
Came here first to this gallery, then the gap,
then died. With me in Highgate and alive.

lxxiv

After his death some friends in London met
at Robert's place. Two men, a girl, and me.
We ate and drank – our voluntary wake,
a show of heart – brave applecart – upset.
Robert read verse on parting by H.D,
the man played blues; the girl (R's ex) would break
and weep, her only visit to the farm
recalling 'La Cigale et La Fourmi'
spoken by Pirie, with his English version,
her language course, a parallel immersion
while he swayed on a wobbly henhouse form.
But all knew what we could not say; his death
impacted, violently, and did deform
our hearts, which fought back, short, all night, of breath.

lxxv

I spoke of Pirie's trout, plays we rehearsed,
then there was Waller's poem, at the start,
not daring to look Pirie in the eye –
and now not able to confront his death,
feared sight once of the best, now of the worst.
Robert then said he thought some works of art
were mirrors to confront such horror by,
how Perseus hid a bright shield underneath
his cloak approaching death on foot alone
to see the Gorgon that he had to kill.
Mirror that had a shape and could contain,
not be, the sight whose truth turns life to stone.
Our way to look hard and draw close until
there, in reflection, lies Medusa slain.

lxxvi

The girl and I sat on the couch, with Robert
cross-legged beside the third guest on the floor.
When he had finished speaking he stood up
and took the tin tea-caddy from the cupboard
then asked us all should he brew up some more...?
– I gestured yes, raising my empty cup.
But why is it so hard to look, I said,
at those who watch us when we act on stage?
It's like the dark taboo, the unturned page
where Orpheus brings Eurydice from the dead.
Out of the audience, Pirie's eyes on me –
mine on the verse – me getting the poem right...
brought us both back to life. Dark in soul-light,
I trusted him. He was Eurydice.

lxxvii

That night I went to bed and had a dream
without an end; it was my fantasy
I think it is this story's end as well.
It dealt with my descent to bring from hell
a living light, a disembodied beam
that might be Pirie or Eurydice.
The story has another ending too,
but waking fact whose meaning must be kept
till after what I finished while I slept.
Though still entirely to do with you,
Pirie, it must touch also on my son.
The dream begins where we broke off the wake.
We hugged and left. I told the girl I'd take
her home to the Embankment, which I'd done –

lxxviii

The Thames was at high tide and black; I'd known
death lay ahead for me; first, taking on
a monstrous role – my face on an all-black swan,
and then – the face which turns the heart to stone.
I was in a dark National Gallery.
I walked and reached the Claude and Poussin room
felt different, somehow hollow in the gloom
looking at different kinds of harmony –
dismay I felt through Poussin for a heart
prepared to meet the last condition of
a grand inquisitor which it must love,
past thought of self, past even thought of art –
colour and light it cost the world to see…
then grief, in Claude whose heart was here in me.

lxxix

Since Pirie's death I'd not dared come. My dream
like some mute sacrifice now came instead,
it was the black swan death sent on ahead
which swam the paintings as across a stream
and stepped these stones to join the living dead.
I dreamt each painting was a stretch of ground
where he had rested, somewhere that would last
stronger than walls. Our joint black stream moved past,
my step, his step; we reached the Underground.
Embankment. There, down there, his cards were cast.
I stood on moving stairs that took me down,
a place of execution and no grace
sometimes in advert-frames I'd see my face
then I saw him rear-mirrored in death's gown.

lxxx

We both stepped off; I stooped to tie my lace.
Pirie stopped too, behind me. I was first
to know this place – descent, in dream reversed,
to torment he must not look in the face.
Perhaps years back on stage when I rehearsed
in poetry what I must now perform –
the way to lead that loved man watching me
somewhere I cannot cry for help, but see
his death through – find the no-love-plat-f-form
check-point of hell – my steps his poetry,
like candles I must blow out, line by line,
to the last breath – then wake. And hell is real.
Go before Pirie, die to his ideal –
light no more ours to shine or not to shine.

lxxxi

His way of death. The last thing. Must I, steel
my heart to feel it, Pirie had dared do
this thing, slunk up to town that day, then threw
this flesh I loved under that hateful wheel –
what self-hate was it, self was me and you
Pirie! I cannot look at you! You look.
There is the light the tunnel starts to throw
we'll meet this train in dream before we go,
read hell headlong in London like a book,
fall between rails, smell terror from below –
the April coffin where we die alive,
Wolf blowing Piggy's house down, sap to stop
us breathing, wheel to rip the grain sacks, drop
the grain to suffocate the farm at five –

lxxxii

where we lie, low, like grain. We are the crop.
We learn our death by heart till we are grown.
Now watch, like corn in death rows to be mown
scattering, haywire! Hell, on earth, up top,
waste – faceless – cuts our gold field to the bone
and black mice pit us with their little nails…!
while over us death's freight train *Springtime* roars
to Highgate where I left my wife, indoors,
asleep, half-singing, like our stream in Wales.
And the cacophony and pain withdraws.

The track goes quiet. We have learned by heart
and come back from the dream, like poetry
whose meaning waits at home. Eurydice,
it's time, our journey through the dark must start.

lxxxiii

Void where we walk but from the back of me
there's light reflected on the tunnel roof:
it's death that mocks us…tempts us…but no proof
is strong enough for hope, Eurydice.
Think, when we first met, acting both, aloof
for fear of losing heart by looking first…
well now we have lost hope – have lived to lose,
to stay the course foregone, postpone the news
ahead. Each step we took in life, reversed.
One path goes home – the one we cannot choose.
Death tempts us subtly at the back of our mind,
a poetry we've loved, yet in this place
forgotten – something dear that had a face
now lost to us. Death lets that shine behind.

lxxxiv

The light we dread is out there in dark space
the two spots on the train that shine ahead
the eyes death sees by blind the living dead
the headlights that annihilate the grace
these are the footlights lighting Pirie's head
at five the evening he plays out his death.
The stage we act on now is not a stage
the page we write on now is not a page
the act of death un-do-able by breath
but done by love to suffer this train's rage
to choose death in its path to feel the verse
stutter and spray off death's wave, break in fear
and crash against our time *c-coming*-near
it pushes, push, *n-no* time to rehearse

lxxxv

pushing us out of will, still pushing, here
hung out of body; hung with no control;
in verse now we have died the death of soul
all hope has gone, words come, words disappear,
we are in hell, all speed is to no goal
and death's the final touch to utter waste
touch with no second chance, touch with no friend,
verse cannot tell an impact without end –

the sight – the train – comes… write… *It can't be faced.*

For sight is endless love. Though horror send
its stone, its numbness, sight's a sacred act.
And when I wonder how to tell this dream
the black swan-neck burned on dead breast – no scream
all throat – all coil on no-man's land – in fact,

lxxxvi

the moral sight, things being what they seem,
made the moment violent beyond speech.
Pirie, when I was young, a sight did reach
this pitch of utter force, my childhood theme.
It rolled like sea. Fast, faster – blur-on-a-beach –
till it stood still. I stood before my father.
Looking from in me, eyes front, was the sense
I knew my life by. Focused. Too intense
to change or to escape. Us. One another
bound in a fate no story circumvents –
our lives unreal, our lives eternally true.
A chain reaction neither pleasure nor pain
but volts, passed through this – arm – chest – to this brain –
once started, shattering layers of me, it grew

lxxxvii

until an impact I could not contain
pushed past the brink of me made flesh by fate
broke in my body, lifted, changed its state –
hurling me free… My father… Watch the train…

A *whumph*. I'm outside time. No time to wait
to hone the shield of poetry in my soul
hammer it, gloss it, to reflect what is
and put it in the hands of Perseus
to watch the worst, the head that has to roll,
Medusa, no – the singer, Orpheus,
still singing as sword swept: head flew from heart
joy's volts still sparkling, down death's stream it fell
singing to her – *Forgive…!* And her *Farewell…!*
had life. Had Pirie's life!
$\qquad$ – the end of art.

PART FIVE

lxxxviii

Far off, still sparkling, was the end of hell.
We were alone, but these sparks seemed to grow,
we watched them, trusting walking here below
brought life our way, and sparks this small would swell
until their flame like seeds the farmers sow
burst into flower. Each tells himself in dream
I know that light behind which powers me
was something I once loved but must not see
and will in time flower into this new beam
not made by sun but by affinity…
And as we stepped into that beam of light
its radiance stilled the violence of the dark;
we slowed…relaxed, like souls that disembark
to meet companion souls, to reunite…

lxxxix

in reeds; trees; swan, sky, chalk-streams – the heart's ark;
the journey ended, here, on Meadows ground.
Like animals, our wonder wrapped us round.
Pirie, I said, *we're here*. This mild remark –
no voice came; stamped – my footstep left no sound.
We walked in silence through this crowd of life
to where, three hundred yards off, someone stood
by the bird sanctuary, a little wood
called Falloden. I'd thought it was my wife
the dream could spirit here, then understood
more than the dream map knew. I recognised
my father, waiting for us. Last-night passed,
the dark play done, reunion, at last,
here in the Meadows. Pleased – but not surprised

xc

he smiled, like dawn, like grain full-grown, new-cast.
Then in our dream I heard my father say
the ode – To Autumn. That September day,
dawn, noon, a dream, no dream, passing or past –
it was the Mercy Scene we came to play.
And all I loved in Keats was there – each line,
the comfort – role-play – singing, always owed
to him, a heart that rose and overflowed
into sufficiency, so we saw love shine,
Pirie and I, as father spoke his ode.
His voice moved through the pilgrim steps of it
and then the light in silence was enough;
on reeds, trees, swan; on us; things spoke their love,
codes spoke their breaking, scrolled in bud to fit

xci

the outspread flower. Depth then shone above.
Leaves' long breaths – singing shapes – stopped in mid-time,
each leaf's intention and each verse's rhyme
showed us the freedom depth was singing of
as father spoke Keats' ode... he seemed to climb
alongside song, he trusted poetry.
Here now was something we three might sustain.
The cup was passed, and time began again,
but still now; song at peace with memory
come from below, the quiet of love's terrain,
where I relive the dream today in mist;
the chapel, the cathedral and St. Cross
all vista clear; orchards in sun-warmed moss,
each apple there, like opening time's fist.

xcii

I don't know how it ended. Mist is loss.
The Meadows vision, Pirie, now the dream
where life came back from death, by this chalk-stream,
Pirie rapt, dad, as-ever-was, the boss –
story that brought to life the real-life theme,
mercy returned from hell. Pa giving me
my soul back lost in death I'd met below.
Pirie then asked him how he came to know
death's timing, and – by heart – life's poetry?
It was a marvel, and we told him so.
Straight-faced, his self-amusement in our hearts,
he told us how his son had loved this verse
and how, at night, with lights out, he'd rehearse
for this performance. Had he served the arts…?

xciii

We laughed. Said yes. And laughter broke the curse
free, in whose thrall this story has been told.
Unfinished Business came in from the cold
and found its stage. Its one-time empty purse
filled by a full house, every ticket sold.
Bar one. For my now not so little son;
who, Pirie, while we played became himself.
Between this poem's drafts we reared that elf
from some midsummer-night's dream; which now done,
I hope he'll find this denizen of the shelf
and read this far, dear son – whose dad I was –
not recognising you, Pirie, of course,
nor his grand-father, Gerald… That dark horse…
But, to his *why I wrote it?* Well… because

xciv

I couldn't get away from death by force,
nor move on through the mist; I felt loss hide
a living friend, a love that hadn't died,
but trusting verse's voice with my remorse
and grief, still struggling against suicide,
brought him back home, like family, to my heart.
Pirie, let's call this mist grief's self-control
that stops us checking up on nature's soul;
let's not, like death with Orpheus, pry, and part
ways with our love; lose, if we must…till art
and dream meet us – dad – Keats, and make us whole.

The other ending of this story's real.
It doesn't have a dream; it's not ideal;
yet I'm not sure dream stops when real lives start

– dreams have real lives. As father spoke Keats' ode
so true that I forgot it was a dream,
I heard the song, the story music told,
told all the time oblivious of the mist
I breathed. While we dream on, things co-exist,
which fall to love, our juggler heart, to hold.
Song can be lost, too, Gorgon stone. No scream.
But when I heard dad speak, song overflowed
into reality, more true not less,
mist, story, dream and poem were one thing
all at once and in turn on the earth we know
where I once stood in joy and in distress;
so I forgot, hearing the poem sing,
that life was accident – song let me go

xcvi

back to the Meadows where all was conceived.
Where now I stand in mist; the story's room
enlarged, swept clean with verse's evergreen broom,
room where all's lost, and dreamt back, and believed...
where time is real; where pattern with needle and thread
guides what returns – brings healing from its source,
heart on the threshold of sun; the poem's course
a story shared between love and the dead
making ends meet; and so my dream was real,
I heard dad speak that verse – and make this space –
for me and Pirie.
       But life too is real.
By which I mean, dear Pirie, it takes place
where we can't see the hand before our face,
here in the mist, and far from that ideal.

xcvii

Remember I told you what some friends feel
about this thing shrinks call the feminine,
a concept you could find no content in,
and thus confirmed their view, your fear to deal
with what was dark, love's chthonic origin…?
Well, I don't think the story quite said all
about the underworld, and death and love;
for there's another child I'm parent of
left by your death, and don't know what to call,
it lives part in the earth and part above.
The Feminine. Can such things be suppressed?
Your death woke a small life suppressed in me
there, years on, loss has set this beauty free –
the child is mine. I feed it at my breast.

xcviii

And look, born when you died, it's almost three.
I know, in England mothers like to wean
a child by now; but this child sucks unseen,
besides they go till four in Germany.
So, I've a little daughter, nameless, lean.
Her father's havoc and her mother, heart.
Born with no love of me to justify
the love I feel for her, she does not cry,
a silent child, a single-parent's part.
I suckle her. She waits for me to die.
What can I do? I love her like my life.
Smaller and older than my little boy
she gives me grief the way he gives me joy,
laughingly. It goes through me like a knife.

xcix

In Gib, they called her father *Death The Goy,*
retired policeman, violent. I met
him only once, a night I won't forget,
a roof-top 70s bar they called 'Me Voy',
'*I'm leaving*'... by the docks, Gib's seediest set...
Death entered. I was dancing unawares
with someone he controlled, who hated him,
a dark-eyed girl called Ina, quiet, slim,
they exchanged words. You know when someone swears.
She said, *Oh, he's a friend*, but sounded grim.
Then up came the proprietor of the bar
and, quite politely, ordered me to go.
And equally politely, I said no.
Our eyes met, held on, pushed too far – too far

c

was fine – it's you or me – *Come on then, throw me out!* But he had no time to reply.
Death hit me, *Back, rat, to your boat and die – !*
threw me down stair boards to the yard below
where, in the car park, I heard Ina cry.
My spectacles were broken, I was scared,
to judge by bottles smashing upstairs, Death
is true to threats it makes beneath its breath,
bars serving Ina would be smashed. None dared.
Ina wept, *It's my fate*, crouched underneath
the dashboard of my car out of his sight.
He'd been in the CID, Oh everyone
was scared of DTG.
                        What your death's done,
Pirie, against love, was conceived that night.

ci

This daughter…all these years beside my son –
this secret sister born at home in grief –
has taught me most. It was her fierce belief
by Orpheus' song in death his will was done;
she wrote *the Mercy Scene,* where life the thief
was understood, where verse speaks truth to life.
But there's no art in her – joy, yes – and loss.
If Robert's phone-call was a hard midwife
we dream now… cottage trees… windfalls and moss…
cathedral – chapel – alms house of St Cross
circle us in their triangle of love.
You know where. Join us. I dream you are here.
Our Meadows. Nothing now we cannot share
in hell, on earth, or this dream…just above.

Acknowledgements

I'd like to record my gratitude to the people who supported and advised me in the various stages of writing The Meadows. Carole Satyamurti and Robert Chandler (the Robert of the poem) from the start believed in the poem and encouraged me, as did Tim Hyman, Christopher Reid, David Black, Jonathon Porritt, Romesh Gunesekera, and Vicky Faure-Walker. This was in the late Eighties. Over the last year, I have revised it extensively and am indebted to Nicky Spice, Martin Taylor, Robbie Lamming, David Matthews, James Greene, my wife, Kate Kellaway and, of course, to Mark Jones for publishing the poem.

I also acknowledge my father, his long reach, supporting me not only with loving memory but the other sort of legacy, and I don't mean poetry.